W9-DIZ-790

THE HOW AND WHY WONDER BOOK OF
MACHINES

By DR. JEROME J. NOTKIN, Science Supervisor, Suffolk County, N. Y.
  Professor, Hofstra College
  and SIDNEY GULKIN, M. S. in Ed., Teacher, New York City
Illustrated by GEORGE J. ZAFFO
Editorial Production: DONALD D. WOLF

Edited under the supervision of
  Dr. Paul E. Blackwood,
  Washington, D. C.

Text and illustrations approved by
  Oakes A. White, Brooklyn Children's Museum, Brooklyn, New York

GROSSET & DUNLAP • **Publishers** • **NEW YORK**

Introduction

The people of very early times may have used machines in primitive ways. As mankind discovered new uses for them, it was able to move from primitive to more civilized ways of living. And the history of civilization almost parallels the ever-widening and ever-wiser use of machines. But, as we learn in this *How and Why Wonder Book,* no matter how complex today's machines appear, they are really combinations of two or more of the six simple ones — the lever, the inclined plane, the wedge, the screw, the wheel and axle, and the pulley.

It is these simple machines which mankind, through the ages, has learned to use in a great variety of ways to help it do its work more easily. This book describes clearly how each type of machine is useful in applying force, in order to make work easier.

A knowledge of simple machines is of practical value to us as we do various daily chores. It also helps us understand and appreciate how the complex machines do their work.

This book, like several others in the *How and Why Wonder Book* series, includes several interesting experiments. By doing the experiments, children will discover some of the laws of machines for themselves and see why it is that we depend on machines to do so much of the world's work.

Paul E. Blackwood

Dr. Blackwood is a professional employee in the U. S. Office of Education. This book was edited by him in his private capacity and no official support or endorsement by the Office of Education is intended or should be inferred.

Library of Congress Catalog Card Number: 60-51559

© 1960, by Wonder Books, Inc.
All rights reserved under International and Pan-American Copyright Conventions.
Published simultaneously in Canada.   Printed in the United States of America.

Contents

The Machine Age

The word "machine" comes from a Greek word, *mechos,* meaning "expedient" or something that makes easy. The Romans used the Latin word *machina,* a word which meant "trick" or "device." The Hebrew word for "machine" is *mechonah,* and as used in the Old Testament and in other Hebrew writings, was variously interpreted as "foundation," "base," "plan." In an age, long ago, when people had to do all kinds of work by hand, it is not surprising that they searched for "expedients" or "tricks" or "plans" to make their work easier. And they found them. Today, so many jobs are done by machine that the age in which we live is often called the Machine Age.

Breaking Through the Language Barrier

A while ago we saw a clown in the circus struggling to lift a chair which had been nailed to the floor by another clown. We could tell how great an effort our clown was making because he got red in the face and started to perspire. No matter how hard he tried, however, the chair wouldn't budge.

Did this clown do work?

Then another clown came out, picked up a feather from the chair and threw it into the air.

Did the second clown do work?

What is work? If your answer to the first question is *yes* and to the second one *no,* you are wrong both times.

Work, as spoken of in this book, occurs only when a *push* or a *pull* moves something with *weight* through a *distance.* The push or pull is called FORCE, and the weight is called RESISTANCE. Remember these two words well. We will need them throughout the entire book.

Going back to our clowns — the first clown tried to apply FORCE

4

(push or pull) to move the weight (the chair), but he did not move it. The second clown applied FORCE (push) and moved the RESISTANCE (the feather, which, however light, has weight) through a distance, by throwing it into the air.

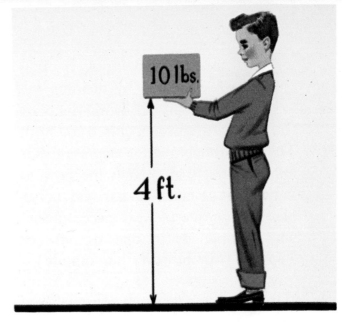

Ten pounds raised four feet equals forty foot-pounds.

When you have finished your home-**How is work measured?** work, you may say that you have done "a lot." In science, we have to be more precise. We can't say: "The machine worked a lot." But we can say: "There was one *foot-pound* of work done." It sounds strange, but it is just another unit of measure. As the foot is a measure of distance, the foot-pound is a measure of an amount of work. We arrive at this measure by multiplying the force by the distance through which it acts.

One foot-pound is the work done by a force of one pound acting through a distance of one foot.

If you lift a weight of ten pounds to a height of four feet, you do $10 \times 4 = 40$ foot-pounds of work, no matter how long it takes.

Which clown is doing work? Answer: The one on the right, because he is applying force and has moved the resistance (the feather).

Power is the rate of doing work. It is

What is power? calculated by dividing the amount of work done by the time required to do it.

The unit usually used to express this is *horsepower*. It is enough for now to know that a machine has one horsepower if its rate of work accomplishes 550 foot-pounds in one second (or 33,000 foot-pounds per minute).

Has someone ever told you that you

What is efficiency? were not efficient in school? In practically the same way, we speak of efficiency of machines.

The efficiency of a machine is the *ratio* (comparative amount) of useful work it does to the total work input.

OUTPUT

INPUT

This picture study will help you understand efficiency.

$$\text{Efficiency} = \frac{\text{Work output}}{\text{Work input}}$$

Because of losses due to *friction* — that is, some form of rubbing action — no machine is able to deliver the same amount of work that is put into it.

Inertia must be overcome before the car rolls and in order to accomplish work.

You may know from having seen others

Why is work hard? try to push a stalled automobile that it is more difficult to get it rolling than to push it after it has started to roll. This is due to the tendency of all bodies at rest to remain at rest. The scientists call this tendency *inertia*. You have to overcome the same inertia to stop a rolling automobile, because a body in motion tends to stay in motion. Thus, you have to overcome inertia to accomplish work.

Ask your friends whether it is easier to lift a pound of feathers or a pound of iron. They might answer wrongly that it is easier to lift the feathers. Measured in terms of work, it is the same. In both cases you lift a weight of one pound. But it is harder to lift two pounds than one pound, because you have to work harder to overcome the weight or the attraction of gravity.

Let's go back to pushing the automobile. If the owner has left the brakes set, it may be impossible to move the

There are many forms of energy — heat, electrical, mechanical and others.

How does energy become active? When energy is used in work, force is applied. This means that force is used to push or pull, to cause a body at rest to move, or to stop a moving body, or make it change its direction, or to cause a moving body to lose or gain speed.

Lift either weight. It's the same amount of work.

car, and if he has left them partly set, it is much more difficult than with no brakes at all. This is due to the rubbing of the brakes against the wheels, or, as the scientists call it, *friction*. Thus, work is hard because matter has inertia and weight, and while working, we have to overcome friction.

Perhaps at some time or other you were **What is energy?** told: "Why don't you do something? You have much too much energy." Well, that's exactly what energy is: the ability or capacity to do something, to work.

Overcoming friction helps the boy (right) to skate.

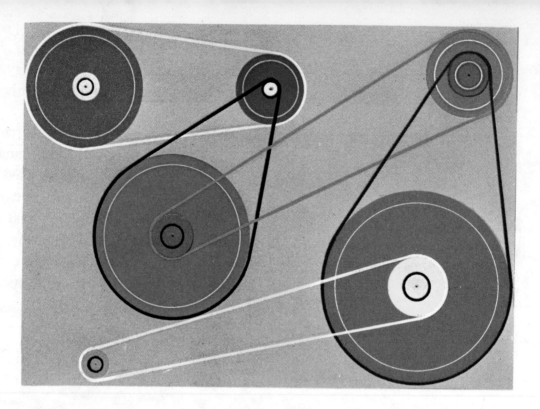

Machines

What, you may ask, has all this to do with the title of this book, the machine? Well, we saw a picture not long ago of a machine with a lot of turning wheels. The machine had a thousand moving parts. When the inventor was asked what this complicated device was supposed to do, he answered, "Nothing at all. It is just a thousand parts in motion."

Was this really a machine? Not in the true sense of the word.

What is a machine? A machine, as we define it here, is a tool or device which, by applying a force (1) makes work easier, or (2) changes the direction of the force, or (3) increases the speed with which work is done. The device with a thousand moving parts, therefore, is not truly a machine, because it is not used to do any work at all.

In other words, we use machines be-

Why are machines used? cause they make possible a gain in *force*—that is, they enable us to overcome a great resistance with a small effort. When this is the case, we say that the machine gives us a *mechanical advantage* of force. Other machines enable us to move the resistance faster than the applied force is used. Such a machine gives us a *mechanical advantage of speed*.

Later on, as we discuss particular machines, we will figure out exactly how big these advantages are.

Living in a time that is called "The

Was there ever a time without machines? Machine Age," it is difficult to imagine that we did not always have the automobile, the airplane, the locomotive and all the other devices man has invented to make his work easier. But there was a time, thousands of years ago, when man had no machines at all, and until not too long ago he relied on the strength of his muscles or the muscles of animals for the energy necessary to operate the simple machines he had devised and constructed.

Even in very early times, man tried to use tools to make

What are the six basic machines?

his work easier. These tools or machines were primitive, and were constructed because of need. In fact, these primitive machines are still used today in one form or another, and even our most complicated modern machines are combinations of the six basic ones already in use early in man's existence. The six basic machines are:

The wedge

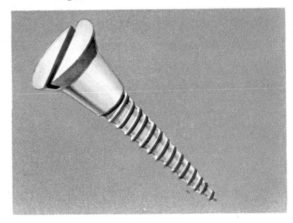

The screw

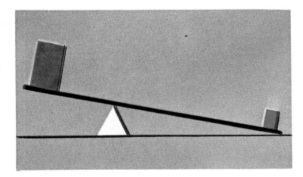

The lever

The wheel and axle

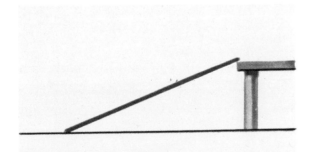

The slope, or inclined plane

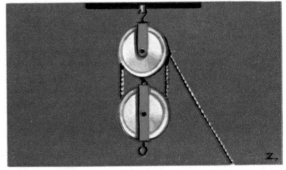

The pulley

The Lever

Can you imagine primitive man trying

How does the lever make work easier?

to protect the entrance to his cave by putting a large boulder in front of it? He is a strong man, but not strong enough to lift the rock — not even strong enough to roll it. Nobody knows who first had the idea — nobody is credited with the invention of this primitive machine, but one day somebody tried to move the stone by resting a long, strong branch on a smaller stone, pushing the end of the branch under the boulder, and pressing down on the branch.

First-class Lever

Can you imagine the pride that man must have felt when he succeeded, without even too much effort, in moving the rock? He did not know that he had invented the machine which we call the "simple lever." By experience, primitive man found that the longer the lever, the more weight could be lifted with less effort. He learned this in the same way you found out where you have to sit on a seesaw to stay in balance, or that the farther you move from the point where a seesaw hinges on its rest,

the easier it is to lift your heavier playmate on the other end. The seesaw, too, is a lever.

The smaller stone in the first picture and the middle point of the seesaw have the same function: to provide a rest for the lever. This rest is called the *fulcrum*. The side where you apply the force is called the *effort*. The opposing side is called the *resistance*.

The lever need not always be straight, like the cave man's branch or the board of the seesaw. Sometimes the lever is

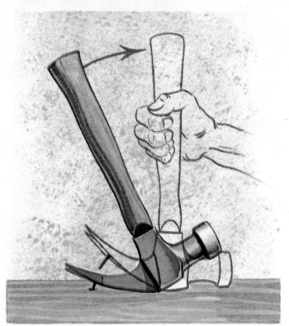

Using a hammer to remove a nail is using a lever.

Early man used the lever, as we have

What is the "Law of the Lever"?

seen, but it was not until thousands of years later —about 240 B.C.—that the Greek scientist, Archimedes, discovered what we call the Law of the Lever: Two loads, A and B, balance when the scale-pan weight of A multiplied by its distance from the fulcrum is the same as the scale-pan weight of B multiplied by *its* distance from the fulcrum. As the force exerted on a machine is called effort, we call the distance from the effort to the fulcrum the *effort arm,* and the distance from the resistance to the fulcrum the *resistance arm.*

curved. When you pull a nail with a claw hammer, you are using a curved lever. The fulcrum is at the head of the hammer. You push down on the handle and the nail comes out. So, you see, we started with a primitive machine and find that it is still in use, in practically its original form, on the playground, in the house, and as part of more complicated machines.

There are three classes of levers, de-

What are the three classes of levers?

pending on the relative position of the effort (E), fulcrum (F), and resistance (R). The first-class lever has F between E and R. Examples of the first-class lever are the crowbar, the seesaw and the pump handle. Now that you know Archimedes'

The boy on the left will have to move closer to the fulcrum to balance the seesaw.

FIRST-CLASS LEVER

SECOND-CLASS LEVER

THIRD-CLASS LEVER

First-class lever: The fulcrum (F) is between the effort (E) and the resistance (R).
Second-class lever: The resistance (R) is between the fulcrum (F) and the effort (E).
Third-class lever: The effort (E) is between the fulcrum (F) and the resistance (R).

Law of the Lever, you can surprise your friends, after you know their weight, by figuring out exactly where you have to sit on the seesaw to balance your heavier or lighter companions — or, better still, where you have to put the lever on the fulcrum to be able to lift them up.

Why are scissors a double lever?

Sometimes two levers are used together to form a double lever. A pair of scissors is such a double lever. The screw joining the two blades is the fulcrum. Try to cut a piece of cardboard with a regular pair of scissors and demonstrate for yourself the Law of the Lever. You will find that if you try to cut with the points of the scissors, you will not succeed. But when you use the scissors so that you cut close to the fulcrum, you will succeed because you have more force.

What is a second-class lever?

We have seen that by using the long end of a lever we get more power and are able to do a hard job using little force. Look at the oars of a rowboat. The ends of the oars are the effort, the oarlocks are the resistance, and the pivotal points of the oars (the ends in the water) are the fulcrum.

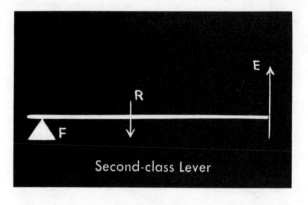

Second-class Lever

Watch closely when you row: The end of the oar in your hand — the effort end — moves farther than the resistance part in the oarlock. There is more force at the resistance. Just as in the case of the seesaw, we move the effort through a greater distance to get, in return, a greater force. So, in both cases, we trade distance or speed for more force. Other common examples of the second-class lever are the nutcracker and the wheelbarrow.

What is a third-class lever?

If you are amazed that you use a lever by riding a seesaw and another kind of lever rowing a boat, think how much more surprising it is that you use the third kind of lever when you fish with a rod. Stop for a moment and try to figure it out for yourself. Does it help if we tell you that in the third-class lever, the effort is between the fulcrum and the resistance? E is between F and R. The end of the

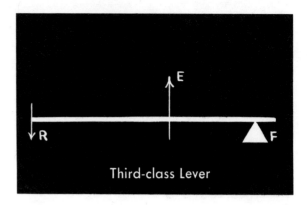

Third-class Lever

fishing pole nearest you is the fulcrum. The effort is the part you are holding and the resistance is at the far end of the pole. Here, for the first time, we exert more force at the effort than there is at the resistance. When you pull a fish out of the water, you will notice that the distance the resistance moves is greater than the distance the effort moves. Sugar tongs, our arms and legs, a broom and a baseball bat are other examples of this type of lever. In the third-class lever, we trade force for more distance and speed.

How You Can Experiment With a Lever

It is fun to check the Law of the Lever with a simple experiment. Build yourself a first-class lever with a ruler, a triangular piece of wood and two stones — a large one and a small one. Now try to figure out the following problems:

(1) where to put the ruler on the fulcrum to balance the two uneven weights.

(2) where to put the ruler to lift the heavier weight.

(3) whether it is possible to shift the ruler along the fulcrum until the weight of the ruler by itself lifts the weight.

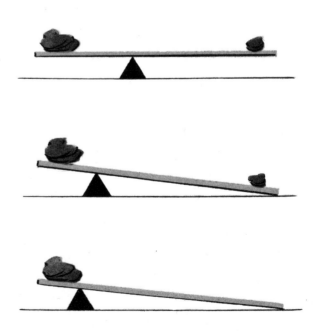

The ancient Egyptians used the principle of the inclined plane when they built pyramids about 4,000 years ago.

The Inclined Plane

Have you ever watched the construction of a large building?

How does the inclined plane help in building?

Have you wondered how so few men do the big job in such a relatively short time? If so, look around the next time and notice the many machines that help the men do their work — the steam shovel, the power drills, the elevators that carry the building materials to the floors high above the ground, as well as other equipment. Now think of the huge buildings of the ancient Romans, the Greeks, and — even earlier — the Egyptians. You surely have seen pictures of the pyramids, the tombs of the pharaohs and their queens. Just imagine these massive structures being built without the help of elevators and steam shovels—with only human effort as the source of power.

Fewer men, less time and more machines are used to build skyscrapers than it took to build the pyramids.

A scientist once figured out that the Great Pyramid, built about 2885 B.C., contains 2,300,000 blocks of limestone, each weighing about two and a half tons. Is it surprising to learn that it took about 100,000 men twenty years to build? How did they manage to get the heavy blocks up to the necessary height? The lever was not much help in solving this problem. They did not have elevators, but they did have the slope, or inclined plane, another of the six simple machines. The inclined plane did not make it possible for them to do the work as fast as our modern machines, but it did make the project possible.

Have you noticed that the long way up a hill is the easier way? It is also easier, as you will have noticed, to go up many shallow stairs leading to the same height. The ancient Egyptians had noticed these things, too, and they built a slope and pulled the stones into place

How does the inclined plane make work easier?

the other end on the floor of the truck. Then he rolls the barrel onto the truck. That is exactly what an inclined plane is: a flat surface with one end higher than the other. A ramp is an inclined plane, and so is a mountain road. The inclined plane is used to help raise a body that is too heavy to be lifted straight up. Just as with the lever, this is accomplished by exerting a smaller force through a greater distance. The

instead of trying to carry them up. They did, on a large scale, the same thing a trucker does today when a barrel is too heavy for him to lift. He takes a flat surface — a heavy board, for example — places one end on the ground and

The stairway leading to the front door of the house on the left is longer than the straight ladder shown in the back of the house. Still, it takes less effort to climb the stairway. The winding road (right) is an inclined plane.

amount of work is the same, whether the inclined plane is long or short, but it is easier to move the load over the longer distance. The less the angle of the inclined plane, the longer the distance and the less the effort needed.

Just as in the case of the lever, resistance times distance equals effort times distance. Now let's do some figuring: Suppose you want to lift fifty pounds five feet above the ground and you have a board ten feet long to make your inclined plane. Since the height above the ground is one-half

How do you figure out the law of the inclined plane?

of the length of the board, you would need only one-half of the weight of the force to pull the weight. In other words, twenty-five pounds of force should lift fifty pounds. Our arithmetic is right, but what about friction, which is the resistance caused when one object moves against another? We are safe in saying that in the example above, it takes a little more than twenty-five pounds to lift fifty pounds, and the smoother the board and the object to be moved, the less the resistance. If the object has wheels, the resistance is even less. That is why moving men usually put heavy furniture on a dolly before putting it on the ramp or other inclined plane.

To find the advantage in using the inclined plane, divide the length of the plane by the height. In our example, the *mechanical advantage* would be ten divided by five, or two.

How You Can Experiment With an Inclined Plane

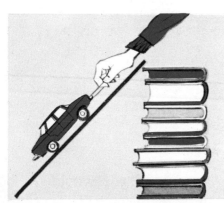

Take a pile of books — about one foot high — and put them on a table. Now attach a rubber band to the front of a toy car, rest your arm on the stack of books, and let the car hang by the rubber band. See how the weight of the car stretches the rubber band to a point where it might even break.

Now take a board, lean it against the books, and pull the car slowly up the inclined plane. You will see that the rubber band will not stretch as far as before, nor will it break.

If you have a spring balance, you can make the experiment even more scientific. Replace the rubber band with the spring balance and you will be able to check on the exact force needed to pull the weight of the car.

The Wedge

When early man used a stone instrument to split the skin

How is the wedge related to the inclined plane?

of an animal, we can be pretty sure that this stone was another of the six simple machines — the wedge. He didn't know at the time that he was using a "basic machine." He knew only that he was using something that enabled him to accomplish a task with less effort. The ancient Egyptians knew much more about the mechanical advantage of the wedge than primitive man. They

Splitting wood is made easier by using a wedge.

put two inclined planes together — back to back — and made a wedge. You could call that a movable inclined plane combination.

The wedge is used to overcome large resistance. You have

How is the wedge used? probably seen the picture called "The Railsplitter," showing Abraham Lincoln using a wedge to split rails. The wedge is hammered into the log and splits it. Actually, all of our piercing tools, such as the ax, the needle, the knife, the carpenter's plane, and many others, are forms of the wedge.

It is easy to understand the advantage of the wedge if you

What is the advantage of using the wedge? think what would happen if the knife or the needle were dull or the carpenter's plane had no blade. However, it is rather involved to figure out the exact mechanical advantage of the wedge as we did with the lever and the inclined plane. This is so because it is difficult to calculate the friction, and because the force applied to this machine is not steady as in the others. The force is intermittent; that is, it is applied in a series of uneven blows or stabs.

The Screw

You have been introduced to the in-

How is the screw related to the inclined plane? clined plane and to its cousin, the wedge. Now let's make the acquaintance of its other cousin, the screw. One of the best, and certainly one of the largest, examples of this simple machine is the staircase inside the Statue of Liberty in New York City. It is a steep spiral stairway which has 168 steps leading up to a balcony in the forehead of the statue. If you look at the illustration, you will see why we call it a giant screw, but can you see why the screw is related to the inclined plane?

A screw is an inclined plane wrapped around a round object such as a pole or a cylinder.

Screws are generally used to hold

The staircase inside the statue resembles a screw.

things together, like the wood screw shown next to the Statue of Liberty. But larger screws can be used for lifting.

Did you ever sit on a piano stool and lift yourself by turning the seat of the stool? Or have you seen an automobile jack in operation? Or, still more thrilling, have you ever seen a house lifted from its site with jackscrews?

What is the pitch?

When the screw is turned once, it advances a distance equal to the space between two grooves. We call this distance the pitch. The mechanical advantage of the screw is equal to the distance which the effort moves in one complete turn, divided by the pitch. When you see a large jackscrew in operation, you will be convinced that the jackscrew provides the greatest mechanical advantage of all the simple machines.

The principle of the screw has practical uses, including lifting houses and cars and adjusting piano stools.

How You Can Make a Screw Out of an Inclined Plane

You will use:

A square piece of paper, 3″ x 3″. Cut it so that you will have two inclined planes.

One round pencil
One colored pencil

Do this:

Color the long edge of the paper shaped like an inclined plane.

Wrap the paper about the pencil.

(Note: The colored edge should resemble a winding road or the colors of a barber pole.)

The inclined plane, of course, is still present. You can prove this by pushing a pencil point along the edge. It will climb the "road."

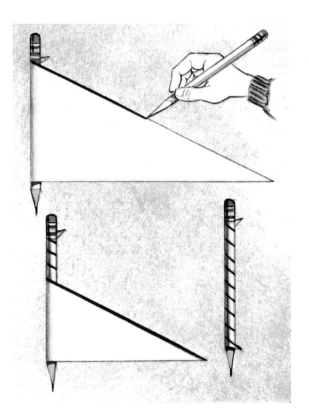

Why We Use Screws

You will use:

Four pieces of wood — from sides of an orange crate

One small nail
One small screw
A hammer
A screwdriver

Do this:

After placing two pieces of wood one on top of the other, hammer the nail in. Make sure they hold together.

Do the same for the other two pieces of wood — but use the screw and screwdriver.

Try to pry them apart.

Which pair is held together more securely? Why?

Which pair required more effort to put together? Why?

Was the extra effort you put into the pair being held together by the screw worth it?

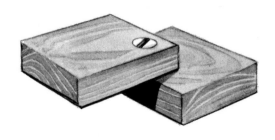

The Wheel

Primitive man made use of logs to move heavy objects.

Why was the invention of the wheel important? Look around you, at home, in the street, wherever you are or go, and just think what it would be like without the wheel. There would be no transportation at all, none of our complex machines and not even most of the simple ones. Even if machines are not all based on the wheel, most of them use it in one or another combination.

What do we know about the development of the wheel? Just as we do not know who invented the other simple machines, we do not know who invented the wheel. We do not even know when and where it was used for the first time. We can assume that early man already had noticed that a round object moved more easily than one that was not round. We may assume that early man used logs to roll loads for short distances, but these were not really wheels.

We know that as far back as 4000 B.C., the Sumerians made use of the wheel. It was a heavy disk connected to an axle. It did not look at all like our wheel of today, but it was round and functioned as our wheel does.

The next improvement came when someone constructed a wheel with crossbars in an attempt to make it stronger.

The Egyptians made bronze wheels with spokes, which were quite strong and much lighter than the earlier wheels. They looked very much like a modern wheel. No doubt it already was

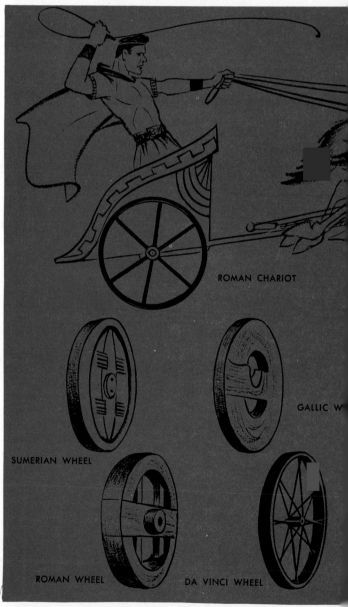

ROMAN CHARIOT

SUMERIAN WHEEL

GALLIC W

ROMAN WHEEL

DA VINCI WHEEL

a wheel rolling on its way to better and finer wheels to make work easier for all.

The Italian painter and inventor, Leonardo Da Vinci, who lived about five hundred years ago, improved the wheel further by making it lighter and stronger than it was.

The wheel in itself is not a machine, but

What makes the wheel a basic machine?

it becomes one when you combine it with an axle or another wheel. Actually, the axle is nothing but a second wheel, fastened rigidly to the first so that the wheel and axle turn together. Let's examine now the principles of the wheel and axle on a machine used by farmers years ago to raise water from the well — the windlass. The picture shows the larger wheel, attached to the axle, being four times the size of the axle; that is, the circumference of the wheel, or the distance around its outer edge, is four times that of the axle. One complete turn of the large wheel will turn the axle one time, since they are attached. If the circumference of the wheel is four feet, you will pull four feet of rope to turn the large wheel once, and wind one foot of rope on the axle. With a windlass, you can lift a bucket with one-fourth the effort.

You can also apply the laws of the lever to the wheel and axle. Going back to the windlass, let's say that if the big wheel makes one turn, it moves through a circle of four feet, and the bucket weighing forty pounds moves one foot up the well. Do you remember the law of the lever? The effort multiplied by the length of the effort arm equals the

The windlass is a combination of a wheel and an axle.

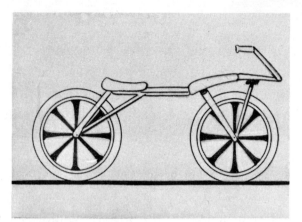

The very first bicycles constructed had no pedals.

Later, pedals were connected to the large front wheel.

resistance multiplied by the length of the resistance arm. In our example, 40 (the resistance) × 1 (the length of the resistance arm) equals 4 (the length of the effort arm) × 10. In other words, an effort of ten pounds raises a bucket of water weighing forty pounds — a mechanical advantage of four.

The idea that was behind the wheel and axle in the example of the windlass was also the idea behind the early bicycle. You probably remember from pictures that the front wheel with the pedals was very large, while the rear one was very small. When the rider turned the large wheel once with the foot pedal, the rear wheel turned many times. For example, suppose the small wheel were only one-quarter the size of the big wheel: When the rider turned the big wheel once with the pedal, the small wheel would turn four times. Such a bicycle would go four times faster than the same bicycle with two of the smaller wheels.

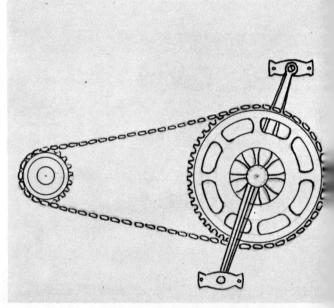

The pedals on today's bicycles turn the back wheel. The chain around this wheel turns the smaller, notched wheel.

You have seen, in the examples of the windlass and the early bicycle, how the wheel and axle work. Now let's examine the modern bicycle. We go easier and faster on the modern bicycle than people went on the early one, with its big front wheel and short rear wheel. Yet the front and rear wheels on the modern bicycle are the same size. It would seem as though what we explained before was wrong, but let's look closer.

How can wheels turn other wheels?

The inventor has attached a notched wheel and cranklike contraption with pedals to turn the wheel, to the front of the bicycle, just comfortably between the front and rear wheels. He also has provided a chain to fit exactly over the notches and a smaller notched wheel to fit the chain on the axle of the rear wheel. This small notched wheel turns with the rear wheel. When the large notched wheel with the chain and pedals is turned once, the rear small notched wheel to which the chain is attached turns many times, thus turning the large rear wheel with it. So we have a more complicated-looking machine, but the same basic principles obeying the same laws.

We do not have to go back to the windlass or the more complicated bicycle to study our problems. The doorknob is also a machine with a big wheel that turns a small wheel, and so is the eggbeater. If you examine the eggbeater, you will see that a wheel with teeth — or cogs, as they are called — engages and moves another wheel with cogs. In the modern bicycle this was done with a chain connecting the two wheels. In the eggbeater there is no connecting chain. Cogwheels that engage each other directly are called gears. Does this ring a bell in your mind? A machine as simple as the gear is an important part of a complicated machine like the automobile.

To make it a little easier for you to

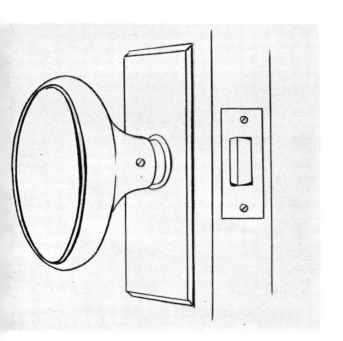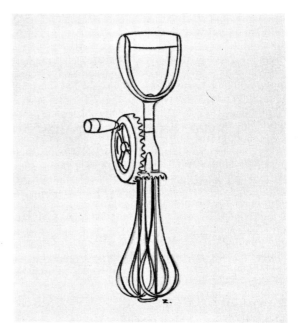

The doorknob and the eggbeater show two practical uses of the combination wheel and axle principle.

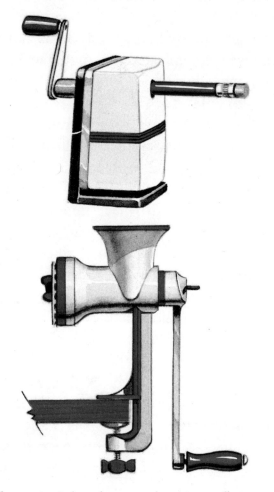

The meat-grinder above needs a longer effort arm.

recognize all the little and large machines that are basically wheel and axle, let us say that you can replace the large wheel by a crank, which acts like a wheel. Does this set the wheels turning? The pencil sharpener, the meat grinder, the crank that started the early automobiles . . . yes, all wheel and axle.

Let's see what we have learned — or better, let's find out what we remember. Yes, indeed, the laws of the lever again!

Why is a meat grinder handle longer than that of a pencil sharpener?

As it is harder to grind the meat than to sharpen the soft wood of a pencil, we need the longer handle or effort arm to achieve our result with as little effort as possible.

Before we explain the one remaining simple basic machine — the pulley — let's first experiment a little with the wheel and axle.

How You Can Experiment With a Wheel

Take a board, drive a nail in the near end, and attach to it a rubber band or — if you have one — a spring balance. Place a weight on the board. Now pull gently on the rubber band or the balance. If you have a balance, you can figure out the force of how many pounds you need to pull the board across the table. If you use a rubber band, you must simply try to

How can you reduce friction?

remember how far the rubber band stretches.

Now put three pencils under the board and pull again. You will find that you need much less force. The rubber band will not stretch as much as the first time.

Now try it again, putting some marbles instead of pencils under the board. The result again will be different.

You have proven that a rolling ob-

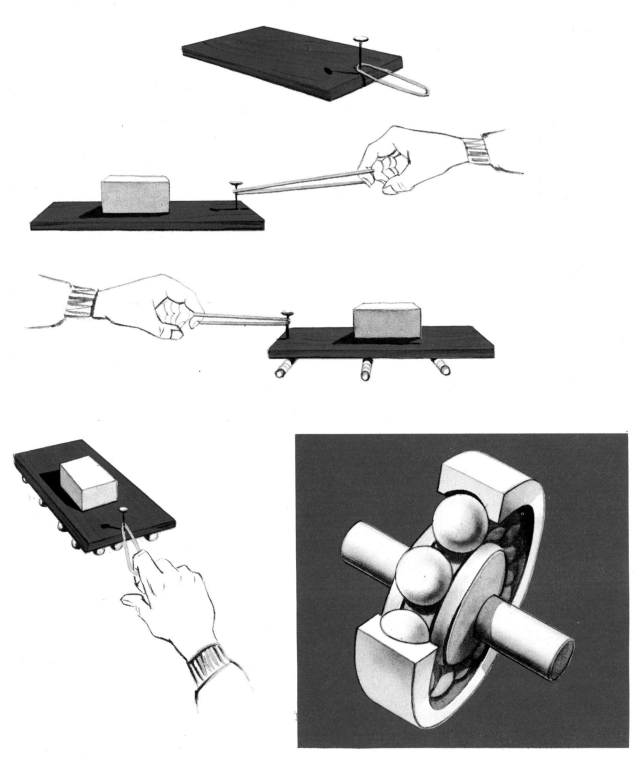

Wheels reduce friction so that the rolling object has less friction than the sliding object. On the right is a cutaway view of a wheel and axle showing the ball bearings (hardened steel balls) which are used to reduce friction.

ject has less friction than a sliding object. The difference between the pencils and the marbles is the same as that between the roller bearings used in heavy machinery and the ball bearings used in the wheels of an automobile.

How to Make a Lift Truck

You will use:

A cigar box
Paper fasteners
Two empty milk cartons (be sure to rinse them thoroughly with cold water)
One pencil with eraser
Scissors
Paper clip
Compass
A knife — or sharp cutter
Small box — about 1″ square
Pliers

Do this:

With the compass, measure off on a sheet of paper a circle about the size of a half dollar.

Make a complete circle and cut it out. Now you have a model of a wheel.

With the scissors, cut out one side of a milk carton. Using your model as a guide, cut out four wheels.

The paper fasteners will serve as axles. Bore a hole in the center of each wheel. Be sure to twist the paper fastener several times through the hole to make it ride easily.

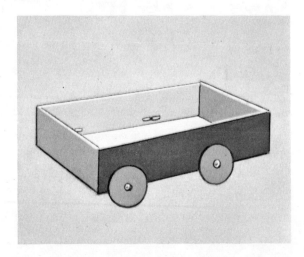

Since most cigar boxes are made of several thick layers of paper — or very thin wood — you will have no trouble making four holes for the axles. You are now ready to attach the wheels to your truck. Put the fasteners through the holes in the sides of the truck and open up the ends inside the box to secure the axles.

Try to roll it. *Hint:* If the wheels are not very sturdy, double them by making another set and stapling them together. If you are very ambitious, you can try making the truck with a cab and open back.

Now you are ready to put the lift wheel and axle into the truck.

Bore two holes through the front of the body of the truck. Put the pencil through them. With the pliers, cut a section of the paper clip. Put one end through the eraser. Now you have a handle for your wheel and axle. *Question:* Which is the wheel and which is the axle?

Tie a piece of strong thread securely to the center of the pencil. If you make a little notch in the pencil, the thread will not slip. By turning the handle of the wheel and axle, you can wind or unwind the thread.

Now you are ready for the track of your lift truck. Cut off one side of a milk carton and bend the two long sides over to face each other.

Cut another piece — the runner — one third the length of the track, but a little narrower to fit into it. Try to see if it fits and rides smoothly. Punch a hole at the top of this runner and tie the end of the thread into it.

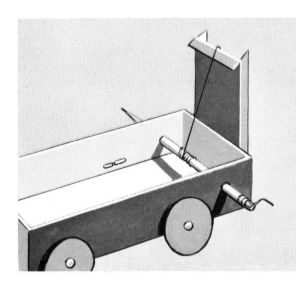

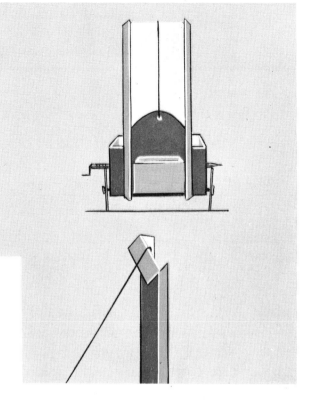

Attach the small box to the runner, either with staples or paper fasteners.

You are now ready to fasten the track and runner and box onto the front of the truck. Your stapler — or paper fastener — will do.

One more hint: Be sure to make a round edge for the thread to glide over the track.

Put some weight in the little box and wind up your wheel and axle. You are now ready to operate a lift truck.

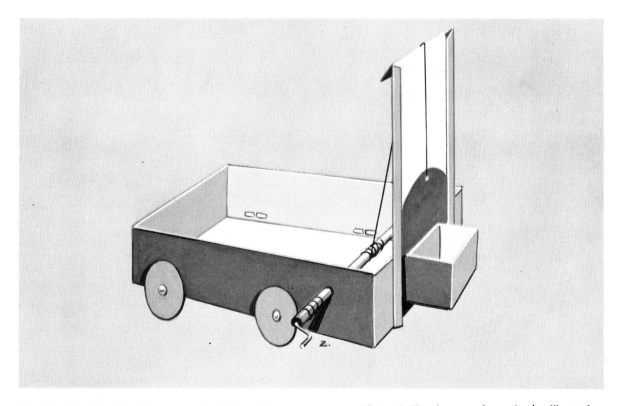

By following the directions, you should be able to construct a lift truck like the one shown in the illustration.

How to Make a Freight Elevator

You will use:

One wooden box
One large dowel stick
Wire hanger
Cord
Small box
Friction tape

Do this:

Remove the cover and base of the box. Make sure that the frame doesn't wobble by reinforcing it with angles. This is going to be a heavy-duty elevator, so it must be sturdy.

Bore two holes about two inches from the top and put the dowel shaft through.

Make a notch in the center of the dowel shaft and tie the cord to it.

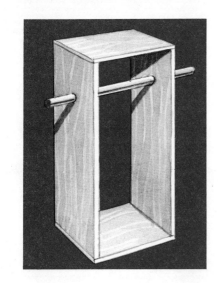

Now cut about six inches of the wire. Bend it into shape. It should be as rigid as possible, since it will serve as a handle for your wheel and axle.

Using the friction tape, wind the handle to the axle — many times, in a crisscross manner. Be sure it is tightly wound. Try it. Does it slip?

Of course, if you have an old handle that you can spare, use it. See if you can be an inventor.

Attach a box to serve as a car for your freight.

Wind the wheel and axle. Do you hear the dowel shaft squeak when the handle is turned? Why? Do you think a bit of grease or petroleum jelly might eliminate the noise? Try it.

If you want to do still better, try attaching a counterweight. Do this:

Place a stone weighing about half a pound in a small plastic bag and tie it with cord.

Instead of tying your cord to the notched dowel, attach the bag with the weight to the end of the cord and let it serve as the counterweight. As the freight car goes down, the counterweight will go up, and the other way round, too.

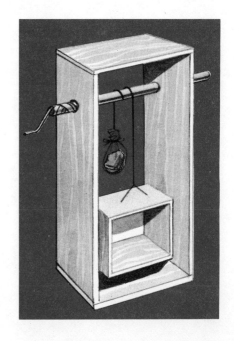

The Pulley

So far, we have made the acquaintance

Why is the pulley often called a wheel with ropes?

of five of the six basic machines. We have learned that machines, whether compound or basic, do not make less work. They enable man to do work with less effort. They make work easier. We have learned that machines are used for greater speed or for greater force — whichever suits the user best. A machine cannot give both increased force and increased speed at the same time. We have seen how the lever best illustrates the value of all machines, because every machine, in a sense, gives leverage (or *mechanical advantage,* as the scientists call it).

Now it is time to meet the pulley, a basic machine that works very much like a first- or second-class lever.

The pulley enables you to raise and lower the flag.

It is a grooved wheel, or combination of wheels, used in combination with a rope or chain to lift heavy weights or, as we shall soon see, to change the direction of a force. We speak of a fixed pulley when the pulley is fastened by means of a hook to some support. A movable pulley is fastened to the weight being lifted.

33

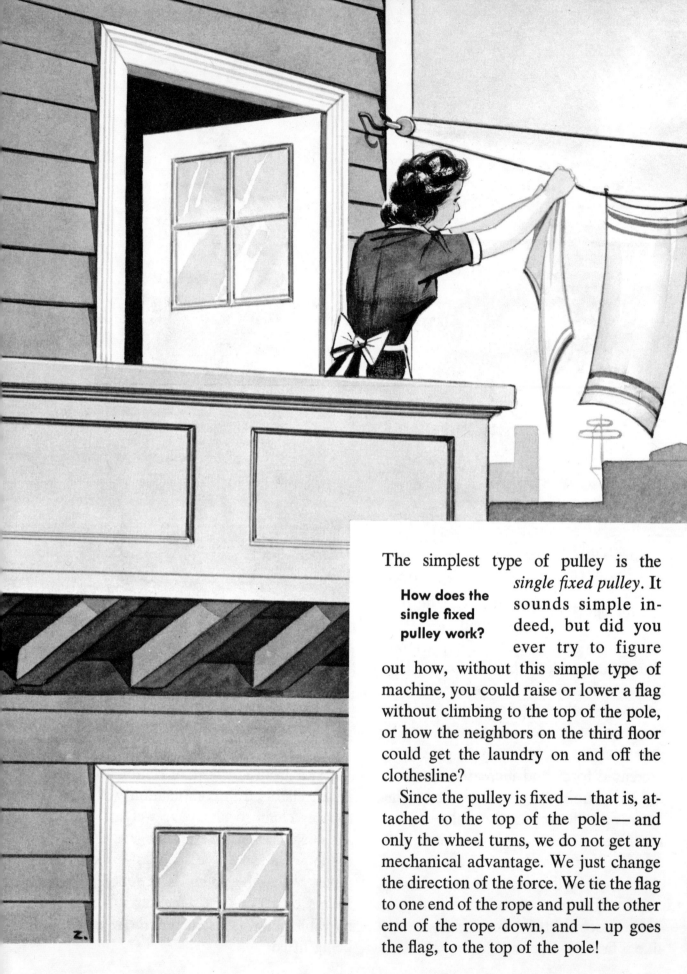

The simplest type of pulley is the *single fixed pulley*. It

How does the single fixed pulley work?

sounds simple indeed, but did you ever try to figure out how, without this simple type of machine, you could raise or lower a flag without climbing to the top of the pole, or how the neighbors on the third floor could get the laundry on and off the clothesline?

Since the pulley is fixed — that is, attached to the top of the pole — and only the wheel turns, we do not get any mechanical advantage. We just change the direction of the force. We tie the flag to one end of the rope and pull the other end of the rope down, and — up goes the flag, to the top of the pole!

The mechanical advantage of the movable pulley is easy to see, especially if you think about what the machine is used for and if you remember your lessons from the inclined plane and the lever. The movable pulley and the combinations we still have to learn about are used to lift weights directly upward. We remember from the story of the inclined plane how difficult this is. You arrange your pulley, as *Figure 2* shows you, fastening the rope on the far end and fastening the pulley to the weight to be lifted, and pulling on the other end.

How is the movable pulley used?

The mechanical advantage of the pulley, like the advantage of all machines, may be obtained by dividing the resistance by the effort. There is, however, another method of determining the advantage, which applies only to pulleys.

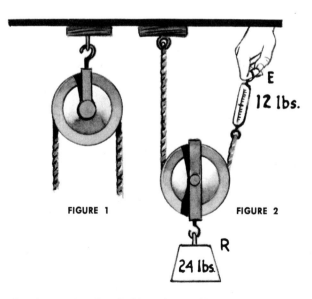

FIGURE 1   FIGURE 2

E
12 lbs.

R
24 lbs.

Single fixed pulley (left) and movable pulley (right)

35

We were interested with our arithmetic to find the mechanical advantage. But let us not forget that in general, in all our figuring, we can apply the law of the lever: Resistance multiplied by the distance it moves equals effort multiplied by the distance it moves. This means that for the pulley in *Figure 2,* for every foot you raise the weight, you have to pull two feet of rope ($24 \times 1 = 12 \times 2$).

You have seen in *Figure 1* the single fixed pulley and in

How does the combination of pulleys work?

Figure 2 the single movable pulley. *Figure 3* shows the . combination of a fixed and a movable pulley, and *Figure 4* shows the combination of two fixed and two movable pulleys.

If you look closely, you will see that in *Figure 1,* the weight is supported by one section of the cord; in *Figure 2,* the weight is supported by two sections; in *Figure 3,* it is supported by three sections; and in *Figure 4,* by four sections. Now let's see how we can arrive at a special method of determining the mechanical advantage.

In *Figure 4,* we see on the spring balance that the pull to lift twenty-four pounds of weight is six pounds, so the mechanical advantage is $24 \div 6 = 4$. Now, remembering that the weight is supported by four sections of rope, we can see that each section actually carries only one-fourth of the load, or six pounds, and that — as you see registered on the spring balance — is the force exerted throughout the entire length of the rope. Thus, in the pulley — and only in the pulley — the mechanical advantage is equal to the number of strands of rope which support the weight.

Now that we have figured together the example for this combination of pulleys, try to do it without help for the other three examples.

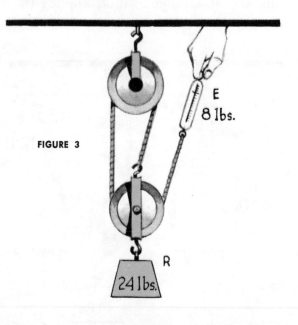

FIGURE 3

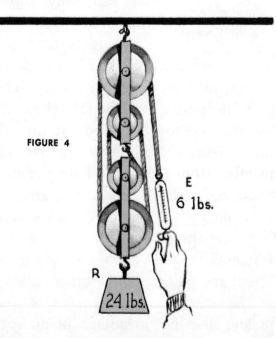

FIGURE 4

Combination of fixed and movable pulleys (left); combination of two fixed and two movable pulleys (right).

Ask two of your friends who are taller

How strong are you?

and stronger than you to grasp a broomstick each and to stand several feet apart. Tie a clothesline to one of the sticks and wrap it several times around both sticks, as the picture shows. Ask them to hold tight to the sticks while you pull on the rope. You

With the help of the pulleys, you can be "stronger."

will see that you will pull the two sticks together and they will not be able to keep them apart. After you have accomplished this, explain to your friends how you did it. Here's a hint: you used a combination of pulleys.

How You Can Experiment With Pulleys

You will use:

Pulley, obtained from a five-and-ten-cent store for about 15¢
About five feet of cord
Small plastic bag
Four-pound weight (rock)

Spring scale
Broomstick or mop handle

Do this:

Put two chairs back to back, about three feet apart.

Place the broomstick across the top of the chairs.

Attach one end of the cord to the center of the stick.

Place the cord through the pulley so that the wheel rides freely, as if the cord were a track.

Place the weight in the bag and tie it.

Attach the weight to the pulley.

Attach the spring scale to the end of the cord and pull up.

This is your own movable pulley, and now you can check all the information that you have learned about it.

What does the scale read? As you know from the previous chapter, it should read two pounds. But it will read a little more than that because here, too, we have to overcome friction.

In the examples on the previous pages you saw a combination of a single fixed and a single movable pulley which was combined so that the mechanical advantage was three. If you do not remember it well, go back to *Figure 3* on page 36 for another look.

Now you should make your own combination, but hang it differently.

You will use:

Two pulleys
A short piece of cord
About five feet of cord
Plastic bag
Four-pound weight
Spring scale
Broomstick or mop handle

Do this:

Put two chairs back to back, about three feet apart.

Place the broomstick across the top of the chairs.

Attach one pulley to the center of the broomstick, using a short piece of cord. This will be the fixed pulley.

Tie one end of the five-foot piece of cord to the broomstick.

Pull this cord through the second, or movable, pulley and up through the first, or fixed, pulley.

Attach the free end of the cord to the spring scale.

Attach the weight, tied in the bag, to the movable pulley.

Pull and read the scale. Again it should read two pounds.

You will have to figure out whether the mechanical advantage is the same or different from your first pulley experiment — and whether it is the same or different from *Figure 3*. Whatever your results, you will find that it was easier to lift the weight — easier than in *Figure 3* and easier than in your own

previous experiment — because you were pulling down instead of up.

If you cannot buy pulleys, you can easily make your own. Cut off both wires of a wire clothes hanger at a distance of about seven inches from the hook. Bend the ends at right angles and slip both ends through an empty spool. Adjust the wires to allow the spool to turn freely and then bend the ends down to prevent the wires from spreading.

We have talked all this time about pulling a weight, pulling on the cord, and so forth. You might think, therefore, that the word *pulley* comes from the word "pull." But it doesn't. If you learn Greek, you will find that *pulley* comes from the Greek word *polós*, which means "axle."

Where does the word "pulley" come from?

39

The Sources of Energy

We have learned that in early times man relied entirely on muscular energy. The first step forward came when man learned to supplement his own muscular energy with that of animals. As man came to rely heavily on horse, ass, ox, and camel, he was slow to discover the uses of other natural sources of energy.

In the beginning of the book it was explained that energy is *the ability to do*

Windmill (above) and water mill (opposite page).

work. It was said that there are many forms of energy. Let's look a little more closely into this now, because energy and man's use of it is the main reason for the development of the machine.

If energy is the capacity to do work, then water moving downhill has energy, the air that moves as wind has energy, and — as we know — we "have energy." What is this energy we have? Can we

What are the different kinds of energy?

make it from nothing? Can we create energy? No. We always have to get it from somewhere. We have to get it from the moving air, the flowing water, or the oxidation of fuel. The oxidation of food provides muscular energy, the oxidation of fuel (when we burn coal or oil) provides energy for the steam engine, and so on.

Matter, as we will learn, may have two different kinds of energy, depending upon whether or not the energy is used or is just there, waiting to be used.

Water going over a waterfall, the weight of the pile driver coming down, steam expanding in an engine, are examples of active energy or, as the scientists call it, *kinetic energy*. The water in a reservoir, the weight of the pile driver resting on top of the machine, are not doing work, but they are in a position to do work. It is not active energy, but stored-up energy or, in the scientific term, *potential energy*.

Thus, kinetic energy is the energy matter has when it is in motion.

Potential energy is the energy matter has because of its position, its condition, or its chemical state.

How Man Harnessed the Forces of Nature

(1) *The windmill.* Man learned long ago to use a sail to catch the wind to drive a boat, but it was not longer than a thousand years ago that he attached the sail to a large wheel. As the wind blew, the wheel turned. This turned the axle to which the wheel was attached, and by using a combination of cogwheels, grindstones could be put in motion to grind grain into flour.

How has man harnessed the forces of Nature?

Later, in the Low Countries of Europe, where large sections of the land are below sea level, windmills were used to pump the water out of the fields. The early windmills had large canvas sails. Today, various improved types of windmills still are in use on farms for pumping water or for generating electricity on a small scale. Modern windmills have metal sails or blades and the wheel is much smaller and lighter. They are constructed in such a way that the wheel can turn freely and always catch the wind, no matter from which direction it blows.

This is a cutaway view of a windmill showing the combination of wheel and axle and cogwheels.

(2) *The water wheel.* While the ancient civilizations of Mesopotamia used crude water wheels to help in the irrigation of the fields, not until the early Middle Ages did the people of Europe develop mills driven by the use of falling water.

In the course of time, several types of water wheels were developed, two of them closely associated with the early days of the American settlers and early American industry.

The *overshot wheel,* as the illustration shows, is turned by water falling upon the wheel from above.

The *undershot wheel* is operated by the force of running water striking the blades of the wheel from the bottom.

A third kind of water wheel was developed by the engineer Pelton and named for him. The *Pelton wheel* is turned by a strong stream of water directed against its blades from a nozzle. The advantage of the Pelton wheel is that it delivers more power than the overshot or undershot wheel and can be operated at a much greater speed.

The most efficient and useful type of water wheel today is the *turbine,* used to generate electricity. It consists of a large wheel with many blades, enclosed in a case or shell. Water piped from a great height first strikes a set of fixed blades attached to the casing, which causes the water to be directed with even greater force against the blades of the wheel and, in doing so, makes the wheel turn with great speed. While a great amount of energy is lost in overshot, undershot, and Pelton wheels, in the turbine the efficiency is more than 90% because of the casing.

From top to bottom: The undershot wheel, the overshot wheel, the Pelton wheel and the modern turbine.

43

How You Can Make a Model Water Wheel

You will use:

A cotton reel or a cork
10 pieces of wood or tin
A meat skewer or knitting needle

Do this:

Use the cork or the reel as the hub of the wheel.

Cut slots down the sides, at right angles to the ends, as shown in the illustration. Slide pieces of wood or tin into these slots.

Use the knitting needle or skewer as an axle.

Hang the wheel in a stand made from a metal clothes hanger.

The stream from a tap in your kitchen or bathroom will provide the water power to turn your water wheel.

This is your finished model water wheel ready for use.

Energy can be changed from one form to another. Here, the boiler sets off the steam engine, which activates the dynamo, which lights a lamp, rings a bell and produces a chemical (electrolytic) reaction.

be traced back to the basic machines. However, only a small amount of the world's energy comes from wind and water. Most useful energy comes from fuels such as petroleum, gas, coal and wood. But only in the eighteenth century did man succeed in developing these sources of energy, and only quite recently did he start to develop the most powerful energy of all — atomic energy.

Wood and coal are burned in a furnace to boil water and produce steam that turns a steam turbine or steam engine; fuels that are liquids or gases can be burned in the combustion chambers of gasoline, diesel, or jet engines; and by "splitting the atom," atomic energy is released.

We have seen now that man has learned

What are some other sources of energy?

to use water and wind as sources of energy to operate machines — more complicated machines than the six basic ones, but still machines that can easily

We have shown you and told you

What is an engine?

about the six basic machines and two early, more complicated machines. We have discussed what makes the machine do work. Let's finish now by explaining the difference between a machine and an engine.

While a machine is any device that

44

makes work easier by multiplying the force, changing the direction of the force, or increasing the speed with which the work is done, an engine is a device that is used to convert some form of energy — usually heat — into mechanical energy.

With this definition, we are near the end of our book, and at the beginning of the machine and atomic age.

Some Important Ideas for You to Remember

Machines have changed our ways of living in many ways — in getting food, making clothing, heating and lighting our homes, and our means of having fun. They have made work easier.

If we understand the simple machines, we can go on to understand the compound machines that are so much a part of our lives. These compound machines can be observed in the home, school, hardware store, toy store, factory, farm, garage and office.

Here are some important ideas about machines for you to remember:

1. If something has to be moved, we have to pull or push it. We use force to bring about movement.

2. We can use more force if we wish to pull or push faster.
3. The force that usually works against us when we push or pull along the ground is friction.
4. When we try to row a boat, we are resisted by the water.
5. Airplanes are resisted by the air through which they fly.
6. This force — resistance — can only be overcome by a greater force pushing against it. If the resistance is greater than the force, then we cannot move our object and no work is done.
7. Work is done only when something is moved.

Some Important Terms for You to Remember

BLOCK AND TACKLE: A combination of fixed and movable pulleys used for hoisting heavy objects.

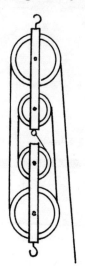

COMPOUND MACHINE: A machine consisting of two or more simple machines.

EFFICIENCY: The useful work done by a machine compared with the amount of work put in.

EFFORT: The force exerted on a machine.

ENERGY: The ability to do work.

ENGINE: A machine that changes energy from one form to another, usually mechanical energy.

FIRST-CLASS LEVER: A simple machine where the fulcrum is between the effort and the resistance, as in a seesaw.

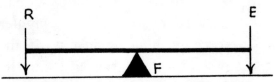

FOOT-POUND: Unit for measuring work done. One foot-pound is work done in lifting a pound one foot.

FORCE: A push or a pull, in order to move something or to stop something from moving.

FRICTION: The resistance that is caused when one object moves against another.

FULCRUM: The pivotal or "resting" point of a lever.

GEARS: Wheels with teeth or cogs that engage other gears.

GRAVITY: The force of attraction between the center of the earth and objects on it or above it.

HORSEPOWER: Unit for measuring power—550 foot-pounds per second.

INCLINED PLANE: A simple machine consisting of a leaning surface along which objects may be pushed or pulled.

INERTIA: The tendency of a stationary object to remain at rest and a moving object to keep moving.

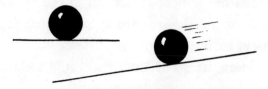

JACK: A machine used for lifting very heavy objects.

KILOWATT: One thousand watts.

KINETIC ENERGY: Energy of an object due to its motion, as a moving car.

LEVER: A simple machine upon which an effort is applied to gain force, speed or distance.

MACHINE: A device used to make work easier.

MECHANICAL ADVANTAGE: The gain in force obtained by using a machine.

PITCH: The distance between the threads of a screw.

POTENTIAL ENERGY: Energy of an object due to its position, as a rock at the edge of a cliff.

POWER: The rate of doing work, usually measured in watts or in horsepower.

PULLEY: A simple machine consisting of a grooved wheel over which a rope passes.

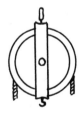

RESISTANCE: The force to be overcome by a machine.

SCREW: A simple machine consisting of an inclined plane wrapped around a cylinder.

SECOND-CLASS LEVER: A simple machine where the resistance is between the effort and the fulcrum, as in an oar.

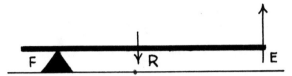

SIMPLE MACHINE: One of the six basic devices used to do work — inclined plane, lever, pulley, screw, wedge, and wheel and axle.

THIRD-CLASS LEVER: A simple machine where the effort is between the resistance and the fulcrum, as in a fishing rod.

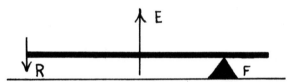

WATT: Unit for measuring electrical power.

WEDGE: A simple machine that is thick at one end and sloping to a thin edge at the other.

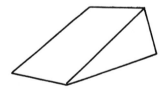

WHEEL AND AXLE: A simple machine consisting of a wheel or crank attached to an axle.

WORK: Applying force to move an object from one place to another.

Even the most complicated modern machines are combinations of two or more of the six basic machines described in this book. The picture above, for example, shows some of these basic machines. How many can you find?

THE HOW AND WHY WONDER BOOK OF
MATHEMATICS

Written by ESTHER HARRIS HIGHLAND, B.A.
Associate Director of Research,
International Statistical Bureau, Inc.

and HAROLD JOSEPH HIGHLAND, B.S., M.S., Ph.D.
Assistant Professor, College of Business Administration,
Long Island University

Illustrated by WALTER FERGUSON

Editorial Production: DONALD D. WOLF

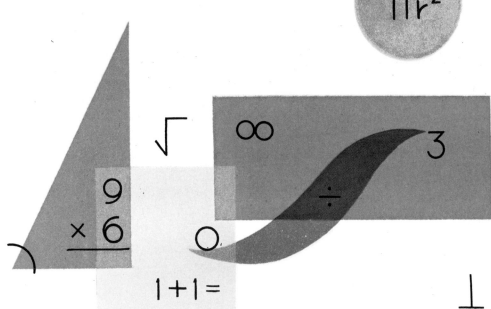

Edited under the supervision of
    Dr. Paul E. Blackwood,
    Washington, D. C.
Text and illustrations approved by
    Oakes A. White, Brooklyn Children's Museum,
    Brooklyn, New York

GROSSET & DUNLAP • **Publishers** • **NEW YORK**

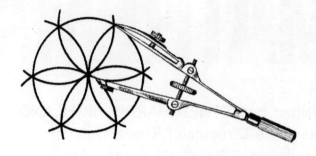

Introduction

If you wanted to find a *googol,* where would you look? In a zoo? Through a telescope? In a deep well? No, you would look in a mathematics book. Mathematics is not only a science in itself, but it is a very important scientific tool as well.

The How and Why Wonder Book of Mathematics is not intended to give the details of arithmetic, algebra, geometry and other branches of mathematics. Rather, it gives an over-all view of what mathematics is, how it developed historically, and some of the ways in which the various branches of mathematics are used. It takes the reader through the story of numbers, from the time when counting beyond two was a struggle for primitive men, to the present time when mathematics can be used to solve tremendous problems of the universe. It answers dozens of interesting questions. How did the stars enter into the development of mathematics? When was the zero introduced? How can you tell directions with your watch? How can you break codes?

Mathematics is a growing, changing tool with many new directions for mankind's use. *The How and Why Wonder Book of Mathematics* points out some of these new directions. It will certainly appeal to young scientists and mathematicians. It will find good use both at home and at school along with the other *How and Why Wonder Books.*

Paul E. Blackwood

Dr. Blackwood is a professional employee in the U. S. Office of Education. This book was edited by him in his private capacity and no official support or endorsement by the Office of Education is intended or should be inferred.

Library of Congress Catalog Card Number: 61-1724

© 1961, by Wonder Books, Inc.

All rights reserved under International and Pan-American Copyright Conventions.
Published simultaneously in Canada.   Printed in the United States of America.

Contents

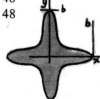

The Language of Mathematics

When you opened this book, you started on a trip through the world of mathematics. In all its long history, mathematics has never been so exciting as it is today. Revolutionary discoveries and remarkable changes are being made more rapidly than ever before.

How do mathematicians communicate?

You would miss much of the enjoyment of traveling through any new land unless you knew enough of the language to understand what was going on. Communicating mathematical ideas was once a problem even among mathematicians, but they solved this by developing a special language. The next few pages will tell you the meanings of the signs, symbols and words which you need to know to enjoy this book fully.

You already know many of them. Just read them — you do not need to memorize them. Refer back to these pages whenever you come to a symbol or word that is unfamiliar. You will soon find that you don't have to look back very often. Although the language of mathematics may be unfamiliar, it is simple to understand.

What is a googol?

If you were walking along the street and found a piece of paper on which was written:

$$googol < \infty$$

would you know that it is mathematical shorthand? The idea of using shorthand or symbols in place of words is very old and is widely used. More than 5,000 years ago, the ancient Egyptians

4

used symbols to stand for words. Stenographers do it today, although, of course, the symbols are entirely different. Mathematical shorthand is a short and exact way of writing mathematical instructions and quantities.

What does "googol $< \infty$ " mean? Translated into everyday English, it reads: *a googol is smaller than infinity.* The little *v* turned on its side means *is smaller than.* Whatever is on the left is smaller than whatever is on the right. The figure *8,* on its side, is the symbol for infinity; that is, a number greater than any we can write, speak or think.

A googol can be written as 10000-0000000000000000000000000000-0000000000000000000000000000-0000000000000000000000000000-000000. It is 1 followed by 100 zeros.

Mathematics is an essential part of our cultural heritage and it has played a vital role in man's history. Men had to learn mathematics to trade, count, sail, fly, build and to send a space satellite into orbit.

It is a number so large that it exceeds the number of raindrops that would fall on New York, Los Angeles and Chicago in more than a century. Yet, it is smaller than infinity.

Signs and symbols are only one portion of the language of mathematics. Definition of basic terms is another. Together they make up a universal language. In this way, a scientist or mathematician writing in France or Russia can communicate precisely with his counterpart in the United States or Great Britain. Googol $< \infty$ has the same meaning to a Canadian as to a Norwegian.

What is a prime number?

Numbers are the basic tools of mathematics. If we multiply two or more numbers, we get a new number. For example, $2 \times 7 \times 11 \times 13 = 2,002$. The numbers 2, 7, 11 and 13, which we multiplied together, are called *factors* of 2,002. However, not every number has factors which are whole numbers. Let us take 13. The only numbers, or factors, we can multiply to get 13 are 1 and 13. If a number cannot be divided, or factored, by any numbers other than itself and 1, that number is called a *prime number*. How about 11 and 37? Both of these are prime numbers. Is 9 a prime number? No, because it can be factored into 3×3 as well as 9×1.

How does algebra differ from arithmetic?

It has been said that the language of science is mathematics and the grammar of mathematics is algebra. *Algebra* comes from the Arabic *al-jabr,* which means the reuniting of broken parts or simplification. Without it, much of our progress would not be possible. Algebra is like a tunnel cut through a mountain — a short cut or the most practical route.

One of the ways in which it differs from arithmetic is that in algebra we use numbers and letters. In algebra, we can say that a case of 50 apples = a. If a man has 10 cases, we write *10a.* Note that we omit the multiplication sign between letters and numbers. At all times the letters represent numbers. If we know the quantity, we generally use a, b, c, etc. If the quantity is not known, we usually use x, y or z. Algebra helps us find the value of unknown quantities by using known quantities.

Another basic difference between algebra and arithmetic is the number of fundamental processes we use. In arithmetic, we use addition, multiplication, subtraction and division. In algebra, we use these four but also *exponents* and *roots.*

Furthermore, in arithmetic, we usually work only with numbers greater than zero, whereas in algebra, we use numbers (or letters that stand for numbers) that are greater or smaller than zero. The numbers that are greater than zero are called *positive numbers.* Those that are smaller than zero are called *negative numbers;* they are written with a minus sign in front of them as: $-x$ or $-43b$.

What is plane geometry?

Plane geometry is a study of the world around us. It is a Greek word which means the *measure of land*. Without it our buildings would be uneven, our walls would not be perfectly upright, we would be unable to navigate through the air or on the seas. Once you are familiar with the basic language of geometry, you will see how easily everything falls into place.

Let us start with a *point*. It indicates a position in space. It does not have width, thickness or length.

A point in motion produces a *line,* of which there are several kinds:

A *horizontal line* is level with the surface of water at rest.

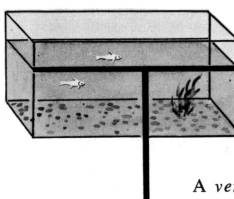

A *vertical line* runs up and down and is at right angles or perpendicular to a horizontal line.

An *oblique line* is neither horizontal nor vertical.

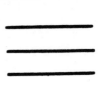 A *curved line* is always changing direction.

Parallel lines are straight lines that never meet no matter how far they are extended.

Angles are formed by two straight lines starting from the same point. Each line is called a *side* of the angle. The point at which the sides join is called the *vertex* of the angle.

 One-fourth of a circle forms a *right angle*. It is ¼ of 360°, or 90°.

An *acute angle* is any angle smaller than a right angle or 90°.

 An *obtuse angle* is greater than 90°, but is smaller than 180°.

A *surface* is a line in motion. It has both length and width but no depth or thickness. A flat surface, like a desk top, is called a *plane surface*.

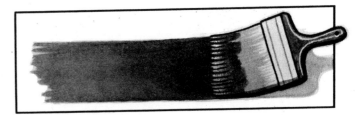

What is a polygon?

One group of plane surfaces is called *polygons*. All their sides are straight lines. If all the sides are equal, the figure is then called a *regular polygon*.

7

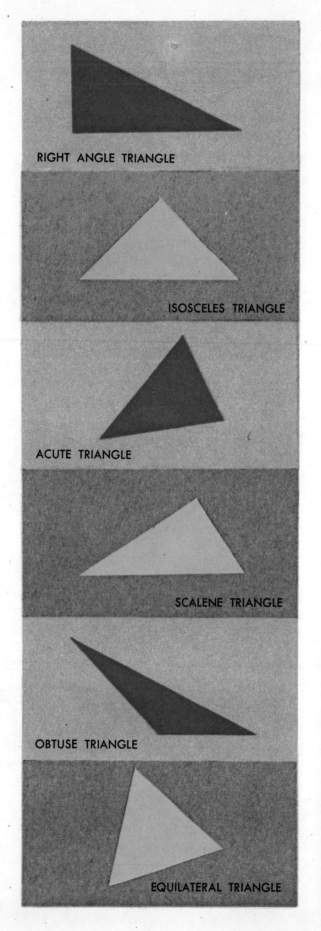

RIGHT ANGLE TRIANGLE

ISOSCELES TRIANGLE

ACUTE TRIANGLE

SCALENE TRIANGLE

OBTUSE TRIANGLE

EQUILATERAL TRIANGLE

The lowest number of sides which can make a polygon is three. This is a *triangle*. There are two basic principles which mathematicians have found that apply to all triangles:

The sum of all three angles of a triangle equals 180°.

The length of the side varies according to the size of the angle opposite it. The longest side is opposite the largest angle.

Basically, there are six kinds of triangles:

A *right angle triangle* has one right or 90° angle. The longest side is opposite this angle.

An *isosceles triangle* has two equal sides. The angles opposite these sides are also equal.

An *acute triangle* has all acute angles; that is, each angle is less than 90°.

A *scalene triangle* has three sides of different lengths.

An *obtuse triangle* has one angle that is greater than 90°.

An *equilateral triangle* has three equal sides and three equal angles.

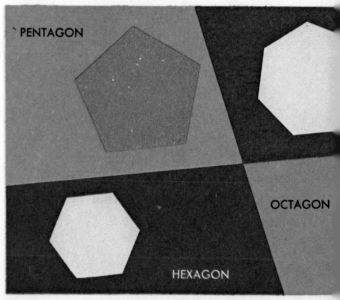

PENTAGON

OCTAGON

HEXAGON

What are quadrilaterals?

Another type of polygon has four sides and is called a *quadrilateral*. The sum of its four angles equals 360°. The sum of the length of its sides is the *perimeter*.

There are six kinds of quadrilaterals:

A *parallelogram* has four sides. Each pair of opposite sides are parallel.

A *square* has four equal sides, and each of its four angles is 90°.

A *rectangle* is a parallelogram with each of its four angles equal to 90°.

A *rhombus* has four equal sides. Two of its angles are obtuse, or greater than 90°.

A *trapezoid* has only two sides that are parallel.

A *trapezium* has no sides which are parallel.

Polygons can have more than three or four sides. For example, a *pentagon* has five sides; a *hexagon*, six; a *heptagon*, seven; an *octagon*, eight; and a *dodecagon*, twelve.

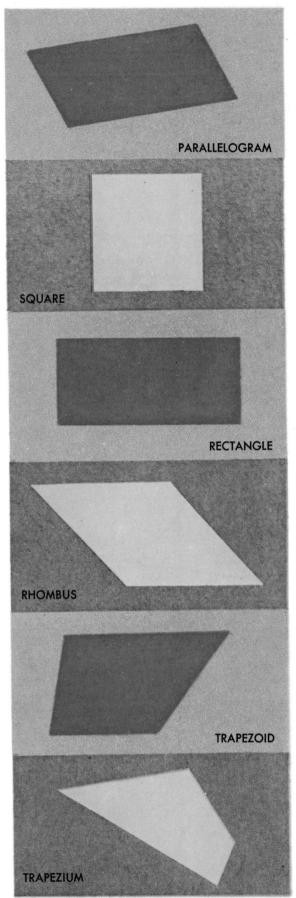

PARALLELOGRAM

SQUARE

RECTANGLE

RHOMBUS

TRAPEZOID

TRAPEZIUM

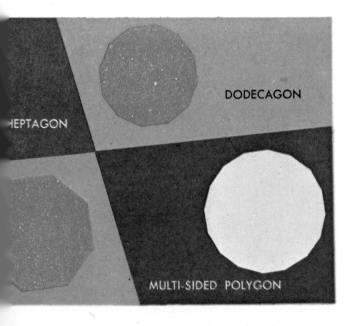

DODECAGON

HEPTAGON

MULTI-SIDED POLYGON

What is a circle?

As the number of sides increases and approaches infinity, the polygon takes on a new shape. It becomes a *circle*. A *circle* is a curved line, every point on which is the same distance from the center. Every circle has 360°.

The *circumference* is the outside boundary.

A *radius* is a straight line from the center to the circumference.

The *diameter* is a straight line through the center of the circle.

A *tangent* is a straight line, outside the circle, that touches only one point on the circumference.

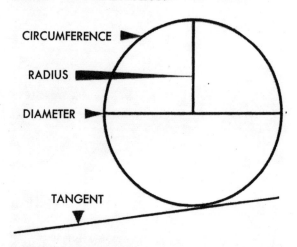

What is solid geometry?

When we add thickness to a surface, we leave the realm of plane geometry and enter that of solid geometry. In this branch of mathematics, we encounter four basic shapes: the *sphere, cone, cylinder* and *polyhedron*.

Polyhedrons are solids with length, width and thickness. Each surface or face is a polygon. There are only five regular polyhedrons:

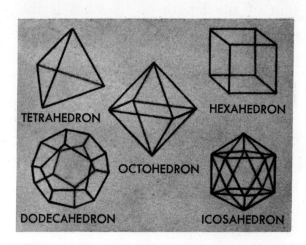

A *tetrahedron,* or pyramid, has four surfaces or faces, each of which is an equilateral triangle.

A *hexahedron,* or cube, has six faces, each of which is a square.

An *octohedron* has eight faces. All the faces are equilateral triangles.

A *dodecahedron* has twelve faces, each of which is a pentagon.

An *icosahedron* has twenty faces. All are equilateral triangles.

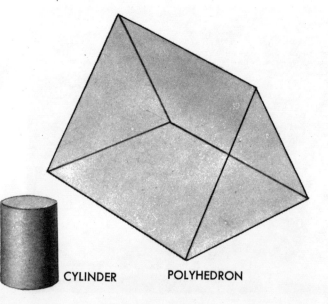

SPHERE   CONE   CYLINDER   POLYHEDRON

Mathematical Signs, Symbols and Definitions

+   *Plus:* sign of addition $3 + 4$

−   *Minus:* sign of subtraction $4 - 2$

× or •   *Multiplication* sign: 4×2 or $4 \bullet 2$

÷   *Division* sign: $8 \div 2$

=   *Equals:* $2 + 3 = 9 - 4$

≠   *Not equal to:* $3 + 4 \neq 4 - 2$

>   *Greater than:* $8 > 4$ or 8 is greater than 4

<   *Less than:* $4 < 8$ or 4 is less than 8

∞   *Infinity:* greater than any number we can write, speak or think

°   *Degree:* unit of measurement for an angle; a complete circle has $360°$

π   *Pi:* used to calculate the circumference and area of a circle; it equals 3.14159

′   *Foot:* used when measuring distance

″   *Inch:* used when measuring distance

′   *Minute:* used to measure parts of a degree; there are $60'$ in $1°$

″   *Second:* used in measuring parts of a minute; there are $60''$ in $1'$

⊥   *Perpendicular to:* forms a right angle

‖   *Parallel to:* continues in a straight line and never meets

What is the language of multiplication?

```
  32     ............Multiplicand: number to be multiplied.
 ×14     ....        Multiplier: number which does the multiplying.
 ───
 128

  32
 ───
 448     ............Product: result of multiplication.
```

What is the language of division?

```
              19   ...Quotient: result of the division.
Divisor:  ......8 |153 ...Dividend: number to be divided by the divisor.
number by which  8
dividend is to be 73
divided          72
              ───
               1  ....Remainder: number left over at the end of the
                      division if the divisor does not divide the divi-
                      dend evenly.
```

What is the language of fractions?

$\dfrac{4}{9}$ . . . . . . *Numerator*: indicates number of parts used.
. . . . . . *Denominator*: term below the line that divides the numerator; number of parts into which the whole is divided.

$\dfrac{6}{7}$ *Proper fraction*: numerator is smaller than denominator.

$\dfrac{13}{4}$ *Improper fraction*: numerator is larger than denominator.

$2\frac{1}{4}$ *Mixed number*: a whole number and a fraction.

What are square roots, radicals and exponents?

$\sqrt{}$ *Radical* indicates the root of a number. It is usually used to indicate *square root*. For example, $\sqrt{4} = 2$, since $2 \times 2 = 4$. A square root of any number is another number, which, when multiplied by itself, equals that number. Here is another example: $\sqrt{16} = ?$ What number can we multiply by itself to give us 16? The answer is 4, since $4 \times 4 = 16$.

$\sqrt[3]{}$ When the radical is used with a small number in the upper left, it stands for a smaller root. For example $\sqrt[3]{27} = 3$, since $3 \times 3 \times 3 = 27$. In the same way, $\sqrt[4]{256}$ stands for the fourth root of 256, or a number multiplied by itself four times to equal 256. The answer is 4, since $4 \times 4 \times 4 \times 4 = 256$.

A small number written at the upper right-hand corner of another number is called an *exponent*. It is mathematical shorthand to indicate the number of times you have to multiply the number by itself. For example: $2^2 = 2 \times 2$ or 4. If we wrote 3^4 we would mean $3 \times 3 \times 3 \times 3$, or 3 multiplied by itself four times.

Numbers and Numerals

We do not know when primitive man first began to use speech instead of sign language to communicate with his family and neighbors, but we do know that man used words for thousands of years before he learned how to set these words down in writing. In the same way, many thousands of years passed after man learned to name numbers before he began to use signs for these numbers — for example, to use the numeral *3* in place of the word *three*.

Men needed numbers and had to learn to count. Maybe it started when

Early man knew "one" and "two." Some primitives (left) used "many" to signify *three*.

Many primitives used pebbles as counters. Peruvian Incas (below) used knotted ropes.

Notching a stick as a counting tool came from early history. Each notch indicated a single mathematical unit.

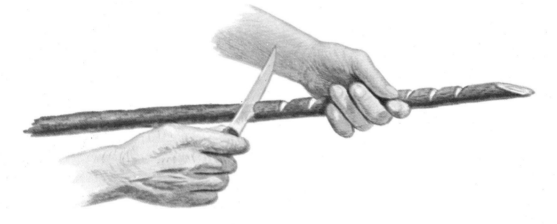

one cave man wanted to trade the saber-tooth tiger he had slain for his neighbor's three spears. Or maybe it started when a twelve-year-old cave-man junior wanted to tell his brothers and sisters about the four hairy mammoths he had seen during the hunt.

What is a number?

At first, primitive man used sign language to indicate the number he wanted to use. He may have pointed to the three spears in his neighbor's cave or to the slain saber-tooth tiger at his feet. He may have used his fingers to indicate the number. Two fingers raised on one hand meant *two* whether he was talking about two spears, two saber-tooth tigers, two caves or two arrowheads.

In everyday usage, we understand that a *number* is a word or a symbol which signifies a specific quantity and it is not necessary to define what we are talking about. For example, *three* or *3* can refer to three airplanes, three pens or three schoolbooks.

How did primitive man count?

Some primitive men did not use numbers beyond two. Only a century ago, when explorers visited the Hottentots in Central Africa, they found that these people had only three numbers: *one*, *two* and *many*. If a Hottentot had three or more cows, even if he had 79 or 2,000, he would count that number as *many*. Most primitive men counted up to 10, or the total number of fingers on their hands. Others counted up to 20, or the number of fingers and toes.

When you count on your fingers, it does not matter whether you start with your thumb or little finger. Among primitive people, there were set rules. The Zuni Indians started to count with the little finger of the left hand. The Otomacs of South America began with the thumb.

As men became more civilized, they used sticks, pebbles and shells to write numbers. They set three sticks or pebbles in a row to show that they meant three. Others made notches in a stick or tied knots in a rope as a means of writing their numbers.

When did man first use numerals?

The earliest written numbers so far discovered were used in ancient Egypt and Mesopotamia about 3000 B.C. These people, living many miles apart, each independently developed a set of numerals. Their simple numerals, 1, 2, 3, were copies of the cave man's sticks or notches. It is interesting to note that in many of the numeral systems found throughout the world, *1* was written as a single stroke (like a stick) or as a dot (like a pebble).

EGYPTIAN	I	BABYLONIAN	Y
EARLY ROMAN	I	CHINESE	—
EARLY HINDU	ϙ	MAYA	•

How did ancient man write?

The ancient Egyptians wrote their numerals on papyrus, a special paper made from reeds, painted them on pottery and carved them into the walls of their temples and pyramids. The Su-

Numbers on Egyptian vases often told their contents.

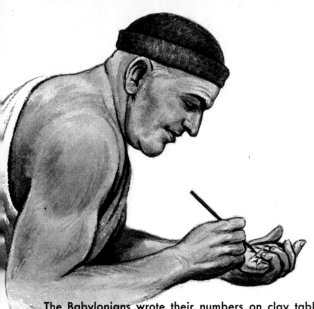

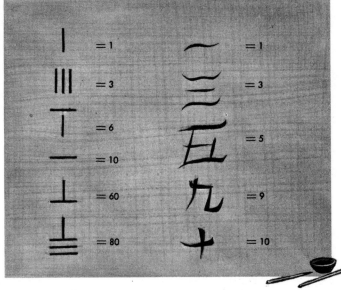

│ = 1		∼ = 1
‖‖ = 3		三 = 3
⊤ = 6		五 = 5
— = 10		九 = 9
⊥ = 60		十 = 10
⊥ = 80		

The Babylonians wrote their numbers on clay tablets. The Chinese wrote numbers with brush and ink on silk.

merians taught the Babylonians how to cut their numerals into soft clay tablets. The ancient Chinese did their number writing with ink and a bamboo brush or pen on cloth.

In the Western Hemisphere, with no contact with the rest of the world, the Mayas of Central America developed one of the most remarkable of the early number systems. They made their numerals using only three symbols: a dot •, a straight line —, an oval Ⓥ .

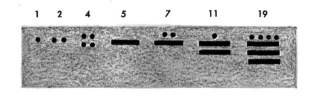

How long would it take you to write a million?

The ancient Egyptians, Babylonians and Chinese, like the early Greeks and Romans, used special signs or numerals to express large numbers. This development of special signs for large numbers was the first advance in numeral writing. Imagine the difficulty and the time needed to write one million by cutting

notches in branches or setting pebbles out in the sand. If you were to follow these methods, or count pennies one at a time (1 a second), it would take you 278 hours, or 11 days and 14 hours of nonstop counting to reach one million.

How did ancient man write large numbers?

Here are several examples of how the ancient people wrote their large numbers:

The ancient Egyptians wrote *100* as ☉ and *1,000* as ⚱ .

The ancient Babylonians used a more complex system. Their numeral for *50* was ⟩▶◁ . This was made of *60* ⟩ , their symbol for minus ▶ , and their numeral for 10 ◁ .

In the ancient Chinese numeral system, the symbol for 100 was 百 while 千 indicated 1,000.

The early Romans wrote 100 as C and this was also used by the later Romans. The early Roman numerals for 1,000 was CIƆ∞ but this was changed to M by the later Romans.

Placing the symbols vertically, one

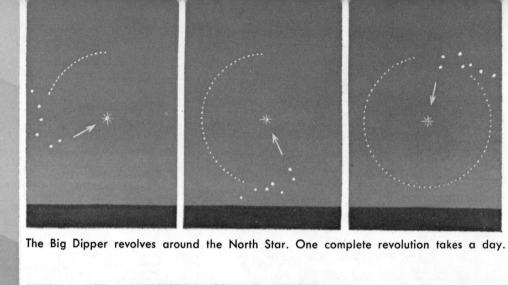

The Big Dipper revolves around the North Star. One complete revolution takes a day.

Early man found his way home at night by walking in the direction of the setting sun.
The rising and setting of the sun was one of his earliest ways of telling direction.

under the other, was the method used by the Mayas to write large numbers. This positioning meant multiply. Their symbol for 100 was ⊘ or 5 — times 20⊘.

Why are numerals important?

Every forward step in civilization brought additional uses for numerals. If a man owned land, he wanted to measure his property. If he sailed in his boat, he wanted to know how far from shore he was. If he wanted to build a temple or pyramid, he had to know how many stones he would need. When he learned to calculate with his numerals, he could measure time, distance, area and volume. By using numerals, he increased his knowledge and control of the world around him.

Mathematics in Early History

How did man first tell direction?

Early man had no towns or villages and he wandered about to hunt for food. Since there were neither roads nor maps, he had to rely on the sun and stars to guide him.

Some men, living along the coast, saw the sun come up from behind the mountains and disappear later into the water. They learned that by walking toward the rising sun, they could reach the mountains, and that by walking toward the setting sun, they could return to shore.

By watching the heavens at night, they found that groups of stars remained together as they moved across the sky. In the Northern Hemisphere, the stars moved in a circle around a fixed point, the North Star. Early man used that star as a guidepost.

How did early man measure time?

The moon was man's first calendar. The moon waxes and wanes; from being almost invisible, it grows to a full, round globe, and then gradually disappears again. Men found that it took about 12 moons, or 360 days, for the seasons to complete one cycle. This was the first measure of the length of the year.

The connection between the regularity of the seasons and the position of the sun and stars was the next observation used to measure the passage of time. By locating the position of a certain star on the eastern horizon just as the sun was setting, it was possible to measure the length of the year more accurately. As early as 4000 B.C., the ancient Egyptians had already set the year at 365 days.

Shadow clocks were the earliest "timepieces." The obelisk or post cast the shadow of the sun. Then the space between the shadow of the rising sun and that of the setting sun was divided. These divisions became the hours.

What is a shadow clock?

The shadows cast by the sun during the day became the first clock. Shadows grow shorter and change direction as the sun rises. Later in the day, the shadows grow longer again. Therefore, the time of day could be fixed by the direction and length of the sun's shadow.

The first shadow clocks, or sundials, were crude. They consisted of an upright stick stuck into the earth, or one stone, or an obelisk mounted on a stone base. These early clocks were both unreliable and inaccurate. If the sun didn't shine, the clock could not be used. Furthermore, since the length of the shadow varied with the season, it was difficult to tell time exactly. It was not until thousands of years later that the sundial was perfected by Moorish mathematicians.

Who were the first practical mathematicians?

The ancient Egyptians, who lived more than 5,000 years ago, are some-times called the practical mathematicians of antiquity, but by modern standards, their mathematics was extremely elementary. At the time they were starting to design and build the pyramids, the Egyptian mathematicians still counted on their fingers. All their arithmetic was a form of either addition or subtraction.

Nevertheless, they did make remarkable contributions to our knowledge of mathematics. Their priests, who were mathematicians, directed the building of temples and pyramids, which served as tombs for the pharaohs. These priests were the architects and engineers who made plans similar to the blueprints used today. These plans called for exact measurements. The crude measurements used by primitive men were not precise enough for the temple and pyramid builders.

How long is a cubit?

To obtain the necessary precision, the Egyptians established a system of measurement based on the human body. The main unit was a *cubit*, the distance from the elbow to the finger tips. Each cubit was divided into seven *palms*, and each palm was divided into four *digits*. According to modern measurements, a cubit equals 18 to 22 inches.

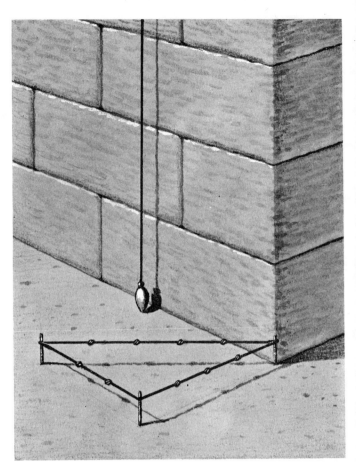

Egyptians used the plumb line and knotted triangle.

How do you make a square corner?

One of the most difficult problems in building the pyramids and temples was to make the base perfectly square. An error would mean that the entire building would be out of shape. The Egyptians solved this by making a *building square*. The first one was probably made by holding a piece of string, with a weight attached to the bottom, over level ground. The string would be perfectly plumb or vertical, and the angle between the plumb line and ground was a perfect right angle. These builders also discovered how to use measuring ropes with equally-spaced knots to make right-angle triangles as guides to building square corners.

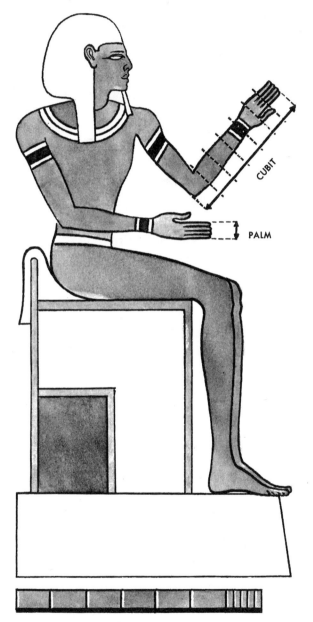

The Egyptian priests made metal bars to correspond to a cubit, with the smaller divisions, palms and digits, indicated on the bars. Today, we would call the bar a *cubit ruler*, marked off in palms and digits, just as our yardstick is marked off in feet and inches.

How did they find the area?

Another problem which the temple and pyramid builders faced was the calculation of area, or how much flat surface is contained within a boundary. Why or when the square was used to measure area is uncertain. Maybe the first clues came from laying square tiles on the floors of the temples. If one room was 8 tiles wide and 8 tiles long, they saw that the room required 64 tiles to cover the floor. Another room 8 tiles wide and 10 tiles long required 80 tiles. From this they learned that the area of a square or rectangle was equal to the width multiplied by the length, or Area = width × length.

Measuring the land required more knowledge of mathematics. The priests surveyed or measured the land because the amount of taxes depended upon the size of the farm, and because the annual flooding of the Nile washed away all boundary stones, making it necessary to measure each farm again and again, year after year.

These farms could not be divided into squares or rectangles easily. They could, however, be divided into triangles. Either by accident or after prolonged study, the Egyptians found that a square or rectangle could be divided into two equal triangles. With this clue, they learned to measure the area of any right-angle triangle. Its area was one-half of the base multiplied by the altitude or height, or Area = ½ base × altitude. Many years passed before they discovered that the same formula could be used for any triangle, even if it had no right angle.

Who were the Mesopotamian mathematicians?

About a thousand miles east of the Nile lies the fertile valley of the Tigris and Euphrates, once known as Mesopotamia. During early history this land was the home of the Sumerians, Chaldeans, Assyrians and Babylonians. In some ways, their society was similar to Egypt's. Their mathematicians also belonged to the priestly caste. Unlike Egypt, Mesopotamia carried on extensive foreign trade with the people to the west in Lebanon, to the north in Asia Minor, to the east in India, and possibly even with China.

What we know of their mathematics comes to us from the baked clay tablets on which they wrote. The Babylonians had advanced mathematical knowledge as far back as 2500 B.C. We know that they inherited from the Sumerians their cuneiform, or wedge-

Egyptian priest-mathematicians (left) surveyed the land after the annual Nile floods, dividing it into triangles.

Man's awareness of the relationship between triangles and rectangles was a step in his quest for knowledge.

shape, writing and numerals. We are indebted to these people for several of our basic mathematical concepts and notations.

When were decimals first used?

The Babylonians introduced the *position system* of numeral writing on which our decimal system is based. We know that the value of any digit depends upon its position in the number. For example, we read *2* as *two*, and *20* as *twenty*. Placing a *2* in the second position to the left means that we automatically multiply it by 10. The ancient Babylonians wrote their numbers in somewhat the same way. Thus, ❭❭ stood for two and ❭❭❬ for 20. Although they introduced the position, or decimal system, into mathematics, it was not until the ninth century A.D. that this system was introduced into Europe by the Saracens.

Who introduced the zero?

It was the Babylonians who first used a symbol for zero. While we have no records of the symbol being used during the early period, there are clay tab-

Babylonian tables included multiplying up to 60 × 60.

lets dating back to 200 B.C. on which the symbol is used to designate the absence of a figure. In their multiplication tables, which contained all the numbers up to 60 multiplied by 60, they used ⟨ as a zero. Since the Babylonians traded with India, it is believed that this concept is the basis for today's zero, which had its origins in India. It was the Moors and Saracens who brought the zero into Europe about the ninth or tenth century A.D.

What is the sexigesimal system?

Another Babylonian contribution to our mathematical heritage, one which has remained in use to this day in astronomy and geometry, is the *sexigesimal* system, which is based on 60. They used this system for their weights and measures. The division of our year into 12 months, the hours into 60 minutes and the minutes into 60 seconds, is attributed to the Babylonians. So is our division of a circle into 360°.

Sailors, Sun and Stars

About 500 miles northeast of Egypt and some 500 miles northwest of Mesopotamia lies the Syrian coast along the Mediterranean Sea. It was here, in the ancient land of Phoenicia, that a seafaring nation thrived more than 3,500 years ago. From the ports of Tyre and Sidon, the Phoenician seamen sailed the Mediterranean. About 3,000 years ago, their ships had passed through the western end of the Mediterranean and undoubtedly sailed northward up toward Great Britain and southward down along the western coast of Africa.

Although their small boats were sturdy, they sailed close to shore to remain near known landmarks. In time, they ventured into the open seas, but only after they had developed the necessary mathematical navigation.

The early Phoenician sailors were among the first to realize that the world was not flat, but curved.

How did the Phoenicians navigate?

The Phoenician seamen, who traveled day after day, never found the ends of the earth. In their ports they could see the tops of the masts of ships as they approached the harbor. Then they could see the sails and finally the entire boat as it came closer to land. At sea, high on the mast, a sailor could see distant landmarks not visible to those on the deck below. They soon realized that the earth was not flat, as many people believed in other civilized parts of the ancient world — it was a sphere. It was many hundreds of years later that the Greeks and Romans used this knowledge to make measurements at sea.

How can you find the distance to the horizon?

This knowledge works for land measurements as well. When you stand on a mountain or a tall building, you have the same view as the Phoenician sailor high in a crow's nest on the mast. How far is *far away*?

Suppose we draw an exaggerated

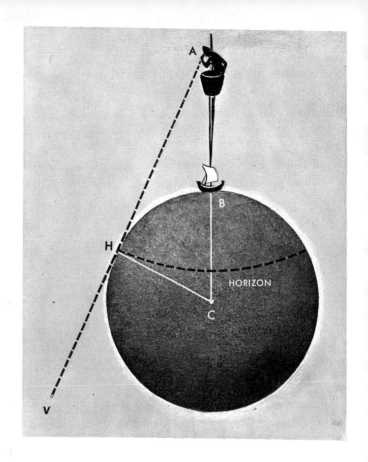

view of you, high in the crow's nest looking out as far as you can see, and we'll also draw the earth.

You are at point A in the diagram.

Your distance above the earth = AB (you are at A and the boat at B).

The line BC is the radius of the earth, a line from the center to the surface. It is about 4,000 miles.

You look toward the point where the sky appears to meet the water, along the line AHV. This line touches the earth at one point only. It cannot touch in two places because this would mean you are looking through the earth. You can turn around and look in any direction, but your line of sight will touch the earth at only one place. If you turn and look in every direction, those individual places would form a circle on the sphere of the earth. We call that circle the *horizon*.

To find the distance to the horizon,

23

we use the mathematical formula: $d = 89.443 \sqrt{h}$ where $d =$ distance to horizon and $h =$ height above the earth's surface measured in miles. Let's try a problem.

You're in a balloon flying 4 miles above the earth. How far is the horizon? We use the formula: $89.443 \sqrt{4}$. The square root of 4 is 2 ($2 \times 2 = 4$) and our answer is $89.443 \times 2 = 178.89$ miles.

How can you use your watch as a compass?

Hold your watch so that it is level with the ground and point the hour hand toward the sun. South is halfway between the hour hand and the 12 o'clock mark. For example, at 5 min-utes after 10 A.M. (Standard Time), with the hour hand pointing at the sun, halfway between the 10 and 12 — or at the 11 — is the location of south. An imaginary line drawn through 11 and 5 points north and south.

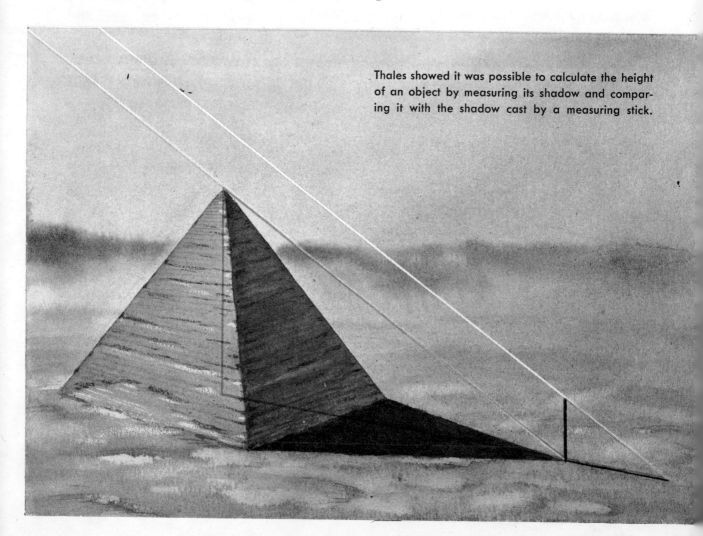

Thales showed it was possible to calculate the height of an object by measuring its shadow and comparing it with the shadow cast by a measuring stick.

The Contribution of the Greeks

There is a belief that mathematics did not become a science until the Golden Age of Greece. Although the Egyptians, Babylonians and Phoenicians brought mathematics a far distance from the days of primitive man, they were interested only in practical math, the computations needed for everyday living, for building, for sailing, for trading. They applied mathematics to specific problems with little or no thought given to basic theories and underlying rules. It was the Greeks who took the giant step from the practical to the theoretical.

Our knowledge of Greek mathematics begins about 600 B.C. when Thales, one of the seven wise men of Greece, introduced the study of geometry into Greece. The Egyptians knew how to measure the height of a pyramid by its shadow, but it was Thales who formulated the basic rule and proved it works in all cases. Demonstrating that a rule is true under all conditions is what mathematicians call *proof*.

How can you measure any height?

You can measure the height of anything using the principles of Thales. All you need is a simple *measuring instrument* which you can make out of cardboard and a piece of wood.

Cut a piece of cardboard 10 inches wide and 11 inches high. Starting along the bottom edge at the right, measure off in inches. If you want more accurate results, divide the space between inches into tenths, using the scale in-

cluded in the diagram. Number the inch marks.

Take a piece of wood, 1 inch × 1 inch, and about 10 inches long. Attach two small screw eyes as shown. Fasten cardboard to the wood with glue or tacks.

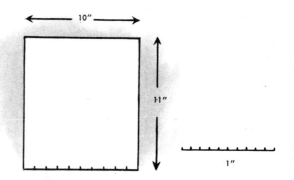

Take a piece of string, 15 inches long, and attach a nail or fishing line sinker to one end. Tie the other end under the wood just at the right-hand edge of the cardboard. You now have a measuring instrument.

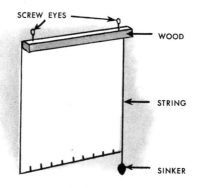

To tell the height of an object, sight through the two screw eyes so that you can see the exact top of the object. The string will hang vertically or plumb. Note the number on the scale that the string touches. Next measure the distance to the object. Multiply this distance by the number on the scale and

divide the product by 10. To this, add the height above the ground that the instrument is held. For example, if the plumb line cuts the cardboard at the *5* mark and you are 60 feet from the tree, multiply $5 \times 60 = 300$. This is divided by 10 so that you get 30. If the instrument is 3 feet above the ground, then the height of the tree is 33 feet.

What is the Pythagorean Theorem?

Pythagoras, who lived about 500 B.C., discovered a basic rule that applies to all right-angle triangles, and proved that it works in all cases, no matter how big or small the triangle is. The *Pythagorean Theorem* states that the square of the longest side equals the sum of the squares of the shorter sides. In other words:
$$3^2 + 4^2 = 5^2$$
$$3 \times 3 + 4 \times 4 = 5 \times 5$$
$$9 + 16 = 25$$
Many of the rules of Greek geometry have come to us from the "Elements," which was written by Euclid about 300 B.C. In its translated form, this textbook was used in many of our schools until about fifty years ago.

26

This simple measuring instrument, like the surveyor's *theodolite*, can help you measure the height of any object. Follow the directions in the text to see how.

How was the earth's size first measured?

The Greek mathematician, Eratosthenes, who lived about 225 B.C., was librarian of the great library at Alexandria in Egypt. He is the first man known to have measured the size of the earth. He applied mathematics to two observations:

At Aswan, near the first cataract of the Nile, it was possible to see the reflection of the sun in a deep well since the sun was directly overhead and cast no shadows on a certain day of the year.

Square of longest side = sum of squares of shorter ones.

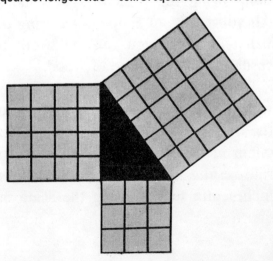

At the same time on the same day, the sun cast a shadow of 7½° in Alexandria, some 500 miles to the north.

Eratosthenes was able to compute the circumference of the earth by using two geometry proofs which earlier Greek mathematicians had developed. First, it was known that opposite angles are equal, and, secondly, it was proven that any straight line that crosses two parallel lines forms the same angle with both lines.

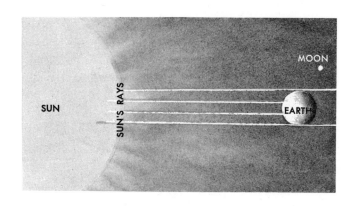

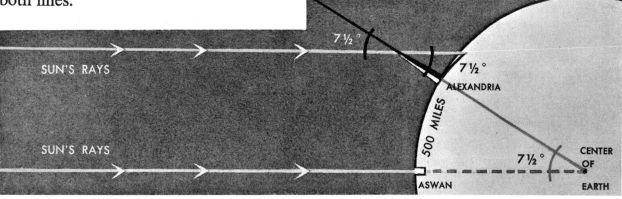

Furthermore, Eratosthenes knew that a circle has 360°. He also knew from his measurements that 7½° was equal to 500 miles on the earth's surface. Since 7½ goes into 360 (the number of degrees in a full circle) 48 times, he multiplied 48 by 500. He computed the circumference at 24,000 miles. With today's precision instruments, we have calculated the earth's equatorial circumference at 24,902.3786 miles.

When did man learn the distance to the moon?

In the second century B.C., Hipparchus, the renowned astronomer of Alexandria, figured out the distance from the earth to the moon. His calculations showed the moon to be about a quarter of a million miles away. He was only 11,143 miles off, since the moon is 238,857 miles from the earth.

What are triangular numbers?

Other Greeks explored the magic of numbers. When adding consecutive numbers, the students of Pythagoras found that they could make rules about their totals. Consecutive num-

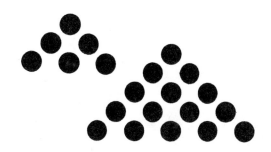

bers formed triangles. To find the sum of any group of consecutive numbers, they created the formula:

$$\frac{n(n+1)}{2} = \text{the sum, where n is the}$$

value of the last consecutive number, where the first number is 1.

What is the sum of the first six numbers? Let n = 6 and using the formula, we find:

$$\frac{6(6+1)}{2} = \frac{6 \times 7}{2} = \frac{42}{2} = 21.$$

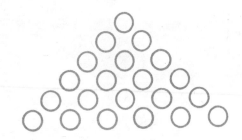

What are square numbers?

You can use checkers or marbles to form any square you wish. The smallest square has one checker or marble. The second square has two checkers in each line. The third had three in each line, etc. The ancient Greeks found that square numbers were related to odd numbers. (An odd number is any number that cannot be divided by two.) If you take the sum of any group of consecutive odd numbers, starting with 1, you always get a square number:

$$1 + 3 = 4 = 2 \times 2 = 2^2$$
$$1 + 3 + 5 = 9 = 3 \times 3 = 3^2$$
$$1 + 3 + 5 + 7 = 16 = 4 \times 4 = 4^2$$

You will notice that the number of odd numbers added is always the same as the number to be squared.

What is a perfect number?

To the Greeks, there was mystery about a number which is equal to the sum of all its divisors, except itself. The first such number is 6 . . . 6 = 1 + 2 + 3. Such a number was called a *perfect number*. The next perfect number is 28 . . . 1 + 2 + 4 + 7 + 14 = 28. The Greeks discovered the first four perfect numbers: 6, 28, 496 and 8,128.

It was not until some 1,500 years later that the fifth perfect number was found. It is 33,550,336. The sixth perfect number is 8,589,869,056. Up to the present, seventeen perfect numbers have been discovered. The last is so long — it has 1,373 digits — that to write it out would take more than half this page.

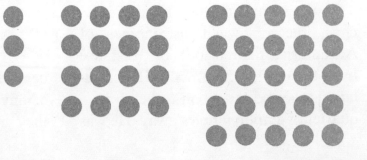

From Roman to Arabic Numerals

At the height of their power, when they had conquered most of the then-known world, the Romans were still not able to master the art of simple arithmetic. Those whose work involved mathematics used three methods of calculation: reckoning on the fingers, the abacus, and special tables prepared for this purpose.

In one respect, the Romans had not advanced far from the days of primitive man, for they still used their fingers to count. Finger counting continued in use for hundreds of years after the decline of Rome, as late as A.D. 1100 in Europe.

How can you do multiplication with your fingers?

Although finger counting had been used for many centuries before them, the Romans, and even the people of the Middle Ages, could only use this method for addition.

Here is an easy way to check your 6 through 10 multiplication tables by using finger reckoning:

Each finger stands for a number from 6 to 10.

To multiply, put the tips of the two number fingers together. (In the illustration, we are multiplying 8 by 8.)

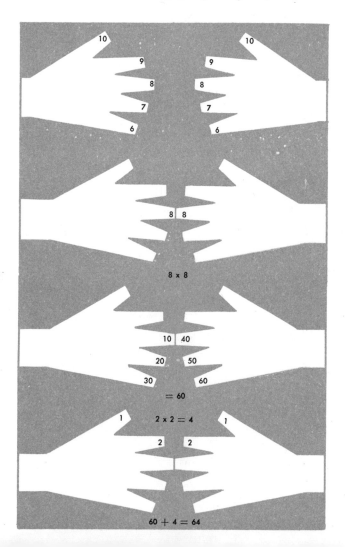

Count by tens the two fingers that touch and all the fingers below them.

Count by ones on the fingers above those that are touching. Count each hand separately. Multiply the ones of one hand by the ones of the other.

Add the tens number to this last number for your answer.

How does the abacus work?

The Egyptians, Babylonians and Greeks used the abacus before the Romans. This simple counting machine was also used by the Chinese and Japanese. Even today, some Chinese and Japanese use the abacus, and they are so expert with it that they can solve problems almost as swiftly as others who use electric calculators.

While the abacus has had many shapes and has had different names, depending upon when and where it was used, its basic operation remains unchanged. It has individual columns with beads or marbles, and these columns are arranged in the numeral-position, or decimal system, of the early Sumerians. The earliest and simplest abacus was a counting board used by the early Babylonian traders.

To add 263 to 349, set pebbles on the board to indicate 263: 2 hundreds, 6 tens and 3 units.

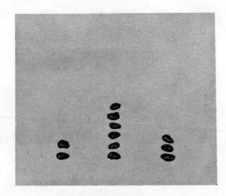

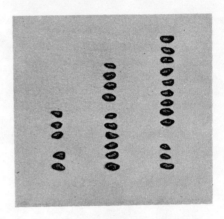

Now add pebbles to signify 349: 3 hundreds, 4 tens and 9 units.

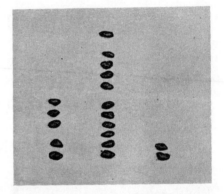

Since no column can have more than 9 pebbles, remove 9 from the units column (on the right), then take another pebble from that column and add it to the tens column.

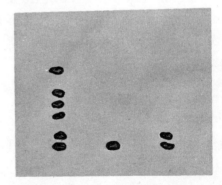

Since there are more than 9 pebbles in the tens column (center), remove the excess over 9 and add one pebble to the hundreds column (left). The pebbles show the answer: 612.

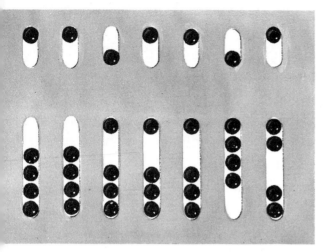

The Roman abacus was made of metal, and small balls were used in each column. To indicate a number, the balls were placed near the divider. The balls on top equaled 5 and the balls below equaled 1 each.

The number shown here is 61,192, using our numeral system.

The abacus in the Orient is called a *suan-pan* by the Chinese and a *soroban* by the Japanese. Moving the beads toward the divider of the frame indicates a number. Here is how 651 would be *written:*

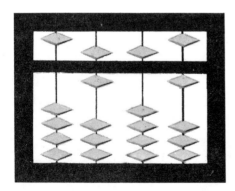

There is a 5 (upper bead) and a 1 (lower bead) in the hundreds column, a 5 in the tens column and a 1 in the units column. To add 152 to 651, move 2 unit beads toward the divider in the

unit (right) column. To add 5 to the tens column, move all four lower beads upward. Since you still need one more to make ten, and since the five or upper bead is already in use, push all the beads in the column away from the divider and add 1 by moving a unit bead toward the divider in the hundreds column. Finally, add 1 bead for the 100 of the 152 you are adding. The beads indicate the answer: 803.

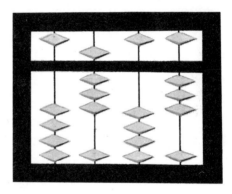

How did the Romans do multiplication?

To do multiplication, the Romans used special tables similar to those used in Egypt and Babylonia. Even with these tables, only highly skilled mathematicians were able to perform multiplication. The Roman numeral system, which is still familiar to us, was difficult to use. Here is an example of how complex even a simple problem could be to the Romans. Let's multiply 18 by 22 using the Roman method:

			XVIII	(18)
			XXII	(22)
			VI	
		XXX		
C	LX			
CC				
CCC	LX	XXX	VI	

CCCXCVI (396) ANSWER

31

The clumsy number systems used by the Romans retarded the development of mathematics. It was not until centuries after the decline of Rome that a new awakening occurred.

What was the greatest contribution of the Hindus?

The Hindu civilization, begun in the valley of the Indus River in India, dates back to the early days of Egypt and Mesopotamia. Hindu mathematics was developed to serve astronomy and emphasized arithmetic. As in Egypt, this knowledge was reserved for the select few, the priests.

The greatest achievement of the Hindus, the one which has contributed most to the development of mathematics as a science, was the perfection of our *Arabic numerals*. Although the Babylonians used a *zero* as far back as 2300 B.C., it is the Hindus whom we credit with the origin of the zero in our numeral system. Their earliest symbol was a dot (.) and this later became a small circle (o) and finally evolved as the zero (0) as we now know it. It is interesting to note that the Hindu word for *zero* means "empty."

The Hindus exhibited great skill in mathematics and did complex problems with very large numbers. The Arabs, who traded with the Hindus, had mastered the Hindu numerical system by the latter part of the eighth century A.D. The Arabs, or Moslems, ruled the Near East, northern Africa and even Spain. It was the Jewish physicians, trained in Moslem schools, as well as the traders, who started the flow of Hindu-Arabic mathematics and numerals into Europe. This knowledge increased greatly during the Crusades, and by the beginning of the fifteenth century, Arabic numerals were widely used by scholars and merchants throughout Europe.

It was this new mathematics — Arabic numerals and the rediscovery of Greek geometry and algebra — that helped Europe leave the Dark Ages and embark on the Age of Discovery.

In India, the Hindus used mathematics and passed their knowledge of numerals to the Arabs.

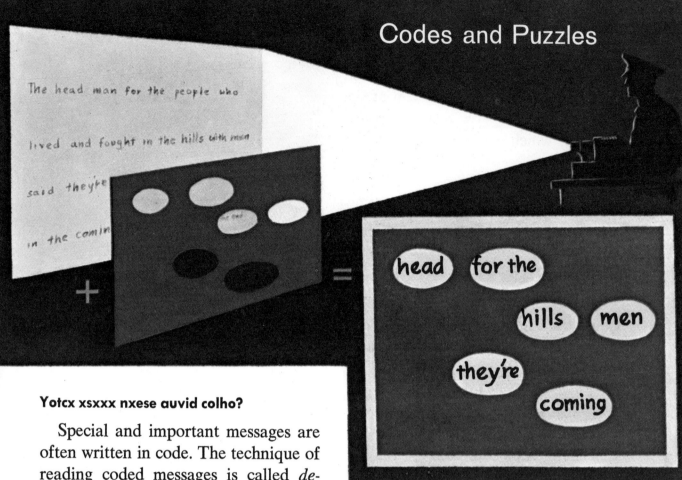

Codes are often used in wartime by military personnel.

Yotcx xsxxx nxese auvid colho?

Special and important messages are often written in code. The technique of reading coded messages is called *decoding*. There are many ways in which you can use mathematics to make and solve codes.

Let's take the message: *Yotcx xsxxx nxese auvid colho?* You will notice that this message contains five words or groups of letters and that there are five letters in each group. This is our first clue. Suppose we try to put the first letters of each word together. We would have: *yxnac*. Certainly that does not mean anything. Neither would we find any meaning if we put the second letters of each word together: *osxuo*. What would happen if we wrote these groups backwards? We would have: *canxyouxso*. We have now found our clue!

This illustrates a *square code*. There are 25 letters in the entire message. It is made up of five words of five letters each. That means that the message was written in a square with five columns across and five rows down. We also know that it was written backwards in its coded form.

If we take the coded message and write it backwards to fit the five-by-five square shape, we would find:

c	a	n	x	y
o	u	x	s	o
l	v	e	x	t
h	i	s	x	c
o	d	e	x	x

33

There is an *x* used between each word and a double *x* at the end of the message. We can now read the coded message, which is: *Can you solve this code?*

How can you make a square code?

It is very easy to make a square code. Count the number of letters and spaces between the words. Find the square root, or number which multiplied by itself gives you this total. If the number of letters in the message is 16, then you use the $\sqrt{16}$ which is 4; that is, four columns across and four rows down.

What if the number of letters and spaces is equal to 59? There is no whole number which, when multiplied by itself, equals 59, for $7 \times 7 = 49$ and $8 \times 8 = 64$. Use the next largest number and add several *x*'s to fill in the blanks anywhere in the message.

All codes are not as simple as this one. Some are very complex and take experts weeks and even months to solve. Here is another one for you to try:

5023355300143500055355100534
3244515000000243401335141500

This one really looks difficult! When you examine it, you find that there are no numbers greater than 5 and that there are many zeros. Does this give you a clue? It wouldn't unless you were a decoding expert. This is a *square number code*. It is made by using a square of 25 boxes:

	1	2	3	4	5
1	a	b	c	d	e
2	f	g	h	i	j
3	k	l	m	n	o
4	p	q	r	s	t
5	u	v	w	x	y

$$z = 66$$

Each letter is composed of two numbers. The first number indicates the row across and the second number shows the column down. Thus *23* is the second row and third column, or the letter *h*. In this code, a zero is used between words. You can use any number of zeros you wish, since they do not stand for anything but spaces. The first number of the message is the code signal. In this case, it is *5*.

Now decode the message. The *50* indicates that a 5-square was used for the alphabet. The first word, using the numbers up to the zeros, is: *233553*. Writing these to form letters, you have: *23 35 53*. Using the code, you can find that *23* is *h, 35* is *o* and *53* is *w*. The word is *how*. You can now solve the rest of the message yourself.

What is a cryptarithm?

The substitution of numbers for letters is called *cryptography,* and a *cryptarithm* is a mathematical problem in which letters are substituted for numbers. Here is a sample:

```
  ABC
  ABC
 ─────
  DBC
  BCE
  ABC
 ─────
 ACDBC
```

The problem is to find the number *ABC* which has been squared. Here is how to go about solving it:

Start with *C* which is the last digit of the number and its square. There are only four numbers, which, when multiplied by themselves, will have their last digit the same as the number. They are: *0* (*0* × *0* = *0*), *1* (*1* × *1* = *1*), *5* (*5* × *5* = *25*) and *6* (*6* × *6* = *36*).

C cannot be equal to *0*, for when you multiply a number by zero, you get zero, but in this problem we multiply *C* by *B* and get *E*.

Neither can *C* equal *6*. Note in the center column of the addition, we have *D* + *C* + *C* = *D*. If *C* equals *6*, it would not be possible to add 6 + 6 + any number and have the sum equal the missing number.

C cannot be equal to *1*, since *C* × *ABC* would equal *ABC*, but in this problem it equals *DBC*. Therefore, *C* must be equal to *5*.

We also know the number of another letter: *A*. We see in the multiplication that *A* × *ABC* = *ABC*. Therefore, *A* must equal *1*.

We now have two digits: *A = 1* and *C = 5*. Write the problem over substituting the known numbers:

```
   1B5
   1B5
  ─────
   DB5
   B5E
   1B5
  ─────
  15DB5
```

Look at the center column where *D* + *5* + *5* is used in the problem. We now know that *10* + *D* equals *D* and we carry *1*. Therefore, we know that *1* + *B* + *B* = *5*. The only number that *B* can stand for is *2* since *1* + *2* + *2* = *5*.

The problem is now solved: *ABC = 125*.

Here is another cryptarithm for you to solve. The answer will be found below, upside down.

```
   DEF
   DEF
  ─────
   FGF
  DEFE
  ─────
  DDEGF
```

Answer to cryptarithm:

DDEGF = 11025   D = 1   E = 0   F = 5   DEF = 105

What is a magic square?

Magic squares have intrigued people for more than 2,500 years. Actually, there is no magic in the square, for it is only an addition table in which the numbers are arranged in a tricky way. Draw a square divided into nine boxes as shown in the illustration.

Now, put in the numbers 1, 2, 3, 4, 5, 6, 7, 8, 9, using each number only once and putting only one number in each box. The numbers have to be arranged so that no matter which way you add them — down a column, across a row or along either diagonal (from one corner to the opposite corner) — the sum is the same.

We know that the sum of all the numbers from 1 through 9 is 45. If you divide this by 3, you will get 15. Therefore, each set of three numbers has to equal 15. Try to solve the magic square before you read the solution below.

How can you make a magic square?

Here is the solution to the magic square problem. You can use this method to make a magic square of any size so long as you have an odd number of columns and rows.

Begin by writing the number 1 in the center box in the top row. Lift your pencil lightly and move diagonally to the right and up. You are now outside the square. Therefore, continue down the next column to the last row. Write the number 2 in that box. Again move diagonally upward and to the right, and again, you are outside the square. Move across the row above to the last box in the square and write the number 3.

8	1	6
3	5	7
4	9	2

The first step in constructing a magic square is shown in red. The second step is in gray. The third is in white.

You have now completed the first set of numbers. A set of numbers is equal to the number of boxes in any column or row — in this case it is three. To begin the next set, move down one box and write the first number of the set, 4. Repeat the same technique used with the first set. Move one box up and one box to the right. Now write the number 5 in that box. Again, move one box up and one to the right. Enter the number 6. You have now completed the second set. To start the third set, go down one box and write the number 7 and then complete the set.

How can you solve the price tag mystery?

Have you ever made a purchase and found cryptic markings on the tag or box? Usually, they are letters, a secret code, which tell the storekeeper the price or age of the product. There is really no mystery as each letter stands for a number. The merchant often selects a name or a word and assigns a letter to each number.

H a r o l d   S m i t h
1 2 3 4 5 6   7 8 9 0

With this code, *ohim* is translated into 4.98 or $4.98. This may be the cost of the object to the storekeeper and he knows that he has to sell that item for more money in order to make a profit. On the other hand, a package may be coded: d h a r h d H — which translated means 6.23.61 or June 23, 1961. This tells the merchant when he bought the product. Note that capital H decodes as 1; a small h decodes as a period. This method of writing code is not new. Both the ancient Greeks and Hebrews used letters to write numbers.

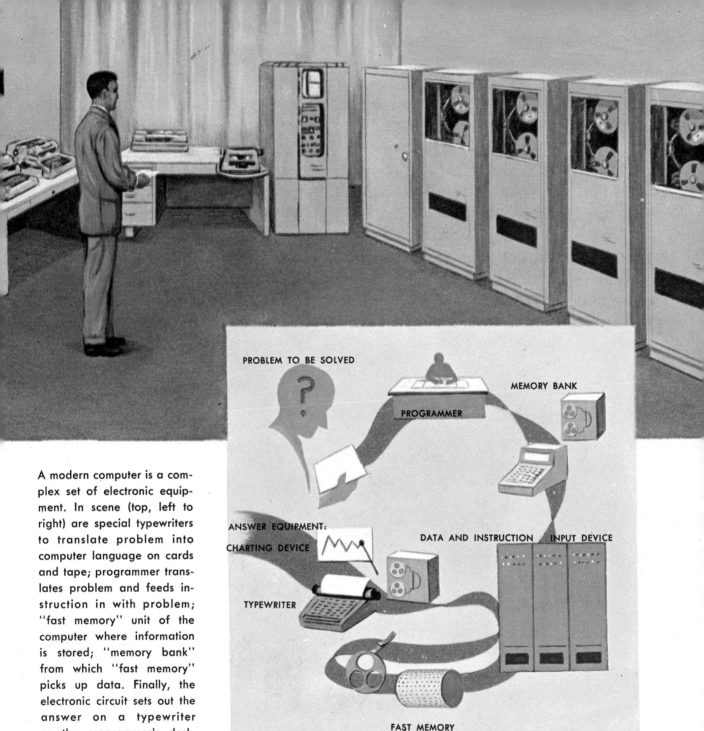

A modern computer is a complex set of electronic equipment. In scene (top, left to right) are special typewriters to translate problem into computer language on cards and tape; programmer translates problem and feeds instruction in with problem; "fast memory" unit of the computer where information is stored; "memory bank" from which "fast memory" picks up data. Finally, the electronic circuit sets out the answer on a typewriter on the programmer's desk.

PROBLEM TO BE SOLVED

PROGRAMMER

MEMORY BANK

ANSWER EQUIPMENT:
CHARTING DEVICE

DATA AND INSTRUCTION   INPUT DEVICE

TYPEWRITER

FAST MEMORY

Calculating With Computers

In minutes, sometimes even in seconds, electronic computers solve problems which would take mathematicians weeks or months to do. Computers today can guide rockets to land on any spot on the earth or to go into orbit around the earth, moon or sun. Computers also help to design and test new airplanes and later guide them through the sky. These modern machines can forecast weather, check the income-tax returns of millions of people, compute payrolls for thousands of workers, and do countless other jobs in only a fraction of the time required by men.

What do *digital* and *analog* mean?

Basically, there are two types of computers: *analog* and *digital*. *Digital* refers to the familiar Arabic numerals which stand for definite quantities. Finding that the sum of $6 + 7 = 13$, is a digital computation. The digits themselves have a meaning, but the units (whether they be chairs, rockets or miles) are not specified.

When we deal with *analog,* there is a basic unit to which we always refer back, like yards, miles or gallons. We say we bought 3 yards of material, or we walked ½ of a mile. The unit of reference is the yard or mile. The numbers 3 and ½ show how many of the units — or what parts of the unit — are being considered.

There are many simple digital and analog computers which are familiar to you. The office adding machine is a digital computer. The fuel gage of an automobile is an analog computer. It indicates what proportion or part of the tank is filled with gasoline.

How does the computer work?

In both the digital and analog computers, the operator punches the instructions (or *commands* as they are called in computer language) and the numbers of the problems on special tape or cards. When the tape or cards are placed in the machine and the power is turned on, the holes in the cards or tape allow tiny electric pulses to travel through and mark the magnetized drum or fast memory of the machine.

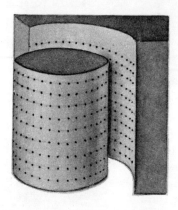

The computer's magnetized drum, known as "fast memory."

The computer takes the information on the drum, draws upon its memory banks, and interprets all the data. It then performs the necessary calculations and puts the results on magnetic tape. The tape is either fed to a special typewriter, which translates the electric impulses into language, or operates a special machine, which draws a chart or graph.

What is the *binary system*?

There are two different mathematical systems used by computers. Some work with the numbers we use all the time, the *decimal* or *ten-base* system. Others use the *binary,* or *two-base* system. Although the binary numbers look

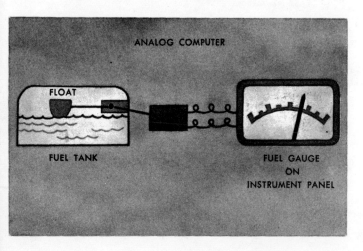

ANALOG COMPUTER

FLOAT

FUEL TANK

FUEL GAUGE ON INSTRUMENT PANEL

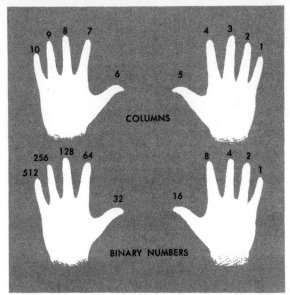

9 8 7
10
4 3 2
1
6 5

COLUMNS

256 128 64
512
8 4 2
1
32 16

BINARY NUMBERS

The position or column in the binary system has a specific value. For example, 100 in binary notation means that the 1 in the third column equals 4; the 0's stand for nothing. Thus, the 100 binary notation = the number 4. Here's another example: 10110 in binary means that the fifth column equals 16, the 1 in the third column equals 4 and the 1 in the second column equals 2. That is 16 + 4 + 2 or 22. Therefore, the binary number, 10110 equals 22.

OUR NUMBER	PANEL LIGHTS			
0	○	○	○	○
1	○	○	○	●
2	○	○	●	○
3	○	○	●	●
4	○	●	○	○
5	○	●	○	●
6	○	●	●	○
7	○	●	●	●
8	●	○	○	○
9	●	○	○	●

Here is how our numbers (zero to ten) would look on a single panel binary computer which has four lights.

Here is a problem: If you saw three panels of binary lights as shown above, would you know what number the machine was showing? The answer is 629.

strange, they are formed in exactly the same way as the decimal system.

The binary computer works on what engineers call a *flip-flop circuit*. It is somewhat similar to the light switch in your room. There are two positions: *on* and *off*. Symbols or numerals are used for these two positions: *1* for *on* and *0* for *off*. If you have a series of switches to turn the panel lights *on* and *off*, you can use different combinations to form various numbers.

Mathematics of the Space Age

What are the space problems of mathematics?

There are many problems in space-age exploration. Some are being solved by psychologists, chemists, physicists and biochemists, but many of the problems are in the hands of mathematicians. Three of the problems which engage the mathematician are:

Computing the varying resistance of the air on a rocket.

Calculating the effects of the earth's rotation on the direction of a rocket or satellite.

Determining initial air speed and momentum force required to counter the earth's gravitational pull.

A rocket speeding through the air of

our atmosphere faces resistance forces similar to those met by a submarine plowing through the depths of the ocean. The faster the rocket goes, the greater the resistance of the air. It has long been known that this resistance increases with the square of the velocity. This means that as the speed is doubled, the air resistance is multiplied by four. It is now known that once the rocket exceeds nine miles per minute, the air resistance increases with the cube of the velocity. In other words, every time the speed doubles after the rocket has reached nine miles a minute, air resistance is multiplied by eight.

If the earth were standing still when a rocket was fired, it would be a simple problem to compute the path of the rocket. However, the earth is constantly in motion. Not only is it revolving on its axis, but it is also moving in an elliptical orbit around the sun. It is necessary to compute the path of the rocket in three dimensions, taking into account the earth's movements, air resistance and the earth's gravitational pull.

With the help of computers, mathematicians carefully plan the path of flight and the increases in speed.

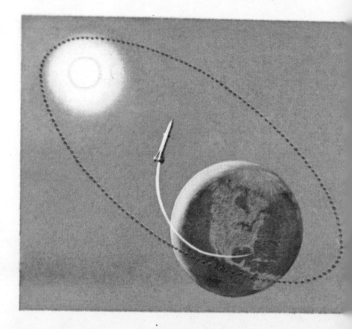

Without gravity, this would be the path of a rocket —
a straight line upward from the loading-firing frame.

Launching a rocket requires precision mathematics.

How does gravity affect a rocket's flight?

We do not know exactly what gravity is, and Albert Einstein, in his *Theory of Relativity,* does not use *gravity* at all. If there were no gravity, we would be able to fire a rocket into the air and its path would be a straight line.

Yet, we know that whatever is thrown into the air or dropped, will come down. We also know that the time for an object to strike the ground is the same whether it is dropped or thrown straight out. Isaac Newton found the precise mathematical formula to measure the force which acts on a falling body, and called it gravity.

41

The formula is $s = \frac{1}{2} gt^2$, where s is the distance an object falls toward the earth, t is the time, and g is the acceleration or increase in speed due to gravity, which is 32 feet per second per each second it falls.

Apply this formula to a rocket fired from a launching pad on top of a very high mountain. The diagram shows how the rocket would fall, due to gravity, if it had no forward speed. It drops 16 feet in the first second, 64 feet in two seconds, 144 feet in three seconds, etc. But the rocket also has a forward speed or initial thrust. Therefore, as it moves forward in its original direction, the pull of gravity acts upon the rocket so that it travels in a curve and finally comes back to earth. The curve made by a body in space is called a *trajectory*.

What keeps a satellite in the sky?

The basic principle of gravity also affects the rocket that will launch a satellite and affects the satellite, too. Using Newton's gravity formula, an object falls 1 mile in 18 seconds. This information helps us to keep the satellite in the sky.

Let us skip the involved mathematics necessary to get the satellite up into the air one mile above the earth's surface. As soon as it gets there, the satellite is affected by two forces. One is its own speed to carry it forward. The other is the earth's gravity pulling it down.

To make the calculation simple, suppose the forward speed of the satellite is 1 mile per second. In the first 18 seconds, the satellite will travel 18 miles along the horizon and will fall 1 mile toward the earth. If the earth were flat, the satellite would hit the earth in 18 seconds, 1 mile from its launching pad. Actually, the earth's surface is curved

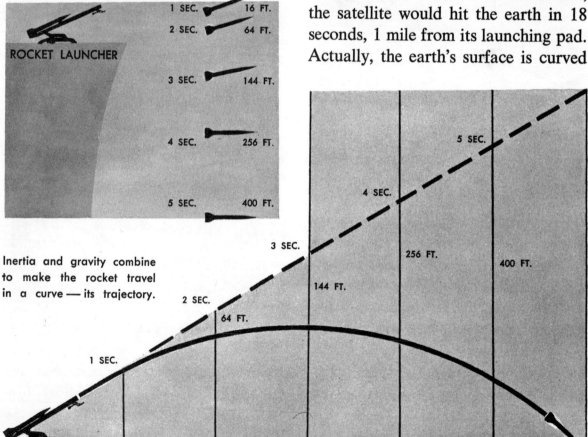

Inertia and gravity combine to make the rocket travel in a curve — its trajectory.

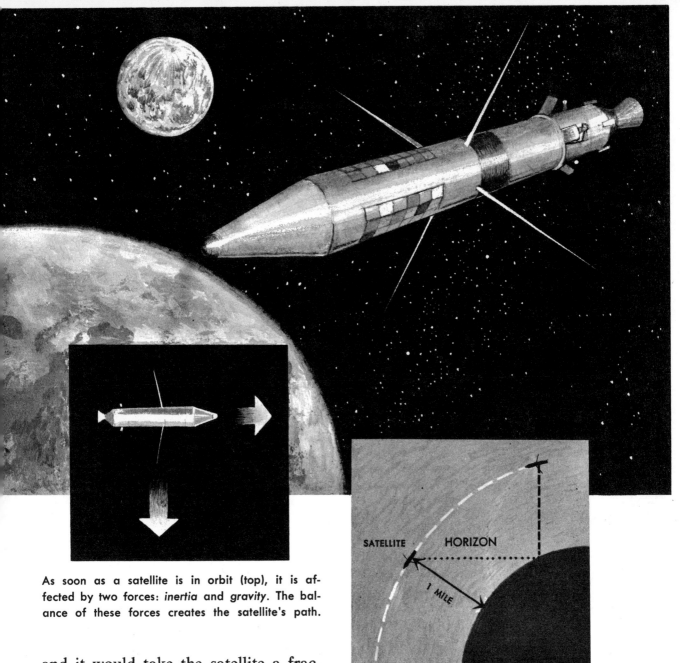

As soon as a satellite is in orbit (top), it is affected by two forces: *inertia* and *gravity*. The balance of these forces creates the satellite's path.

SATELLITE   HORIZON

1 MILE

Speed needed to orbit satellite: 18,000 mph.

and it would take the satellite a fraction of a second longer than 1 second before it hits the earth.

The problem is to determine how fast the satellite must go so that it orbits around the earth. We know that it will fall 1 mile in 18 seconds. Its speed must be so great that it would remain 1 mile above the earth's curved surface. At this point, it would travel 90 miles in a horizontal direction in 18 seconds and reach a point where the earth's surface is 1 mile below. This speed is equal to 18,000 miles per hour.

Even at that speed, however, it would not really be possible to keep the satellite in motion, since we have not considered air resistance. In addition, we have to shoot our satellites to heights of 100 miles or more so that they do not burn themselves up in the earth's atmosphere. At this height above the earth, the air is thinner — there is less friction and less heat.

What Is a Graph?

Rene Descartes, a mathematician who lived in France at the time that the Pilgrims came to America, was the first to use a *graph*. It is a drawing which tells its story through lines, bars, circles and figures. Graphs can show negative and positive numbers, like profits and losses, or degrees above and below zero. Statisticians use graphs to convey a message in its simplest form.

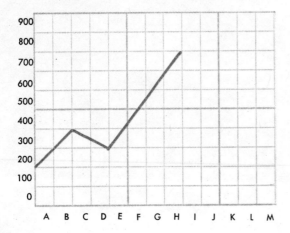
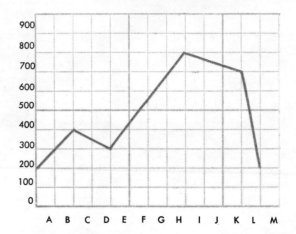

"How's business?" These line graphs tell the answer.

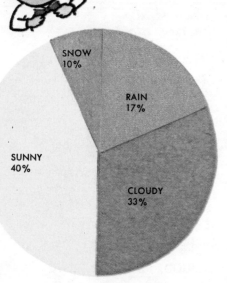

A pie graph shows parts of a whole.

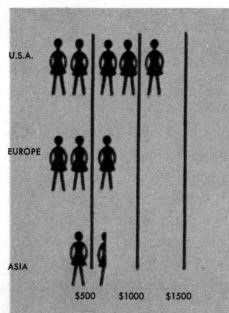

A pictograph gives basic information by using pictures.

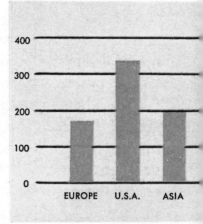

A bar graph is a comparison of two, three or more items.

What Are Your Chances?

What is probability?

When you toss a coin into the air, it will land either *heads* or *tails*. If you toss a penny, what are your chances that it will fall *heads* up? Suppose you tossed two pennies at one time. What are the chances of both falling *heads* up? Are your chances the same in both cases?

If you flip a single penny, it will fall either *heads* or *tails*. The mathematician would say that the *probability* of the penny landing *heads* up is ½ or *one-of-two*. Or, you have one chance out of two that it will fall *heads*.

On the other hand, if you flip two pennies at the same time, there are four ways in which they can land. They can fall with two heads, one head and one tail, one tail and one head, or two tails, as shown in the illustration.

PENNY #1

PENNY #2

Orange stands for "heads"; yellow stands for "tails."

There is one chance of four that any one of these combinations will occur. The probability would be ¼, or one-of-four, for two heads, ¼, or one-of-four, for two tails, and 2⁄4, or ½, or one-of-two, for a head and a tail.

How good is your hunch?

When you guess that the coins will fall with both heads up, you are usually playing a hunch. There is no reasoning behind your guess. But statisticians put probability to work to take the guessing out of hunches. What would happen if you tossed three coins into the air at the same time. You would find the following possible combinations:

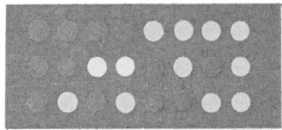

COIN #1

COIN #2

COIN #3

Orange stands for "heads"; yellow stands for "tails."

There are eight possible combinations. The chances of getting all three coins to fall with their heads up is ⅛, or one-of-eight. This is the same for getting all three tails. But the chances of two heads and one tail is ⅜, and the chances of two tails and one head is also ⅜.

Were you to continue tossing an increasing number of coins, you would be able to determine the chances for any possible combination.

What is Pascal's triangle?

Mathematicians have figured out the chances for an almost unlimited number of combinations. These chances are usually presented in a triangular form, known as *Pascal's triangle*. To learn your chances, refer to the proper line of the triangle. For example, if you are to play two games of tennis against a

```
              1   1
            1   2   1
          1   3   3   1
        1   4   6   4   1
      1   5  10  10   5   1
    1   6  15  20  15   6   1
  1   7  21  35  35  21   7   1
1   8  28  56  70  56  28   8   1
1   9  36  84 126 126  84  36   9   1
1  10  45 120 210 252 210 120  45  10   1
```

player who is just as good as you are, what are your chances of winning both games? Look at line two (from the top) of the triangle. According to the *laws of chance* as stated in Pascal's triangle:

You have ¼, or one-of-four, chances to win both games.

You have ²⁄₄, or ½, or one-of-two, to win one and lose the other.

Finally, you have ¼, or one-of-four, chances to lose both games.

If you want the possibilities for eight games, refer to line 8 and you will find that you have ¹⁄₂₅₆, or one-of-two hundred fifty-six, chances to win all eight games.

There is a very interesting number pattern in the Pascal triangle. Each number is the sum of the two numbers immediately above it.

New Mathematics

The fastest growing and most radically changing of all the sciences today is mathematics. It is the only science in which most of the theories of 2,000 years ago are still valid and in which there is still room for new ideas and new branches of mathematics.

What is topology?

One of the most active branches of mathematics today is *topology*, a form of geometry. It is a departure from the Euclidean geometry of rigid lengths and angles and shapes that never change. Topology does not consider size but only shape, and the shape can be folded, stretched, shrunk, bent, distorted in almost any way, but never torn. It has been said that since all solids pierced by a hole look alike to a topologist, he is a mathematician who cannot tell the difference between an automobile tire and a doughnut.

What is a Moebius strip?

Here is a sample of simple topology. Cut two pieces of paper about 1 inch wide and 10 to 12 inches long. Draw a line down the center of each strip. Take

one of the strips of paper and join the ends together with cellophane tape or

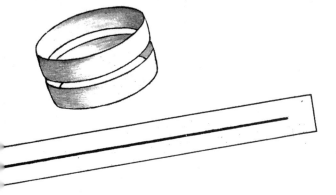

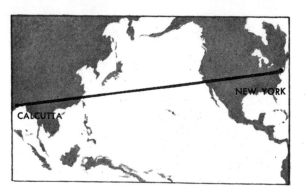

paste. Use a scissors and cut along the center line. You have two rings.

Now take the other strip. Give it a half-twist and join the ends. Take a scissors and cut along the center line.

What do you have? One large circle! This is a *Moebius strip,* named after the German astronomer of the early nineteenth century, Augustus Ferdinand Moebius, who first investigated the curious properties of topology.

When is a straight line not a straight line?

Mathematicians define a straight line as the *shortest distance between two points.* If you looked at a flat map of the world and used a straight line to find the shortest distance between New York and Calcutta, India, you would find that the path goes across the Atlantic Ocean to Morocco, across Africa, the Arabian Sea and India.

But the world is not flat. Instead, if you find the shortest distance on the surface of a globe, the path goes northward over Canada, Greenland, the Arctic Ocean above the top of Europe,

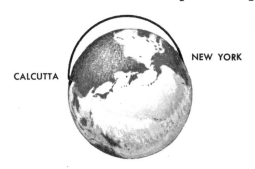

over Soviet Siberia, Tibet and Nepal into India. This is called the *Great Circle route* and it is, indeed, a strange straight line, since it curves with the curvature of the earth.

How do you do the *impossible?*

Here is a problem which cannot be solved with ordinary mathematics. There are three houses near each other. Connect each of the houses with the water, gas and electricity supplies so that no lines cross each other.

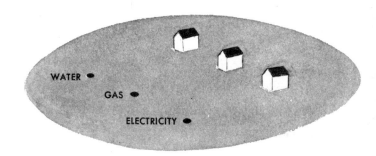

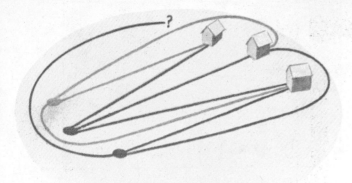

This answer involves topological mathematics. It has been found from experience that no matter how complicated the map, no matter how many countries it contains, and how the countries are situated, the map can be colored by using only four separate colors. However, no mathematician thus far has been able to produce the mathematical proof that this is true.

With the Euclidean geometry of flat surfaces, we could arrive at a situation as shown in the diagram — all but one of the lines connected. You can try other possibilities yourself and see if you can do it.

Using the mathematics of topology, the solution to this problem — as described in the diagram — is exceedingly simple. We use a *torus* or doughnut surface, instead of a flat or plane surface.

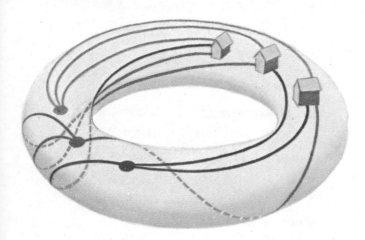

How many colors do you need to color a map?

In coloring maps, it is customary to use different colors for any two countries that have a common boundary. What is the minimum number of colors a mapmaker needs?

Where is mathematics headed?

Mathematics is an essential part of the cultural heritage of our world. New rules are being formulated and new fields — non-Euclidean geometry, algebraic topology, linear programming, matrix algebra, game theory probability — are being explored and developed. In this space age, changes are taking place not only in practical, applied mathematics but also in theoretical mathematics. There is still much ahead in this special field of science. The need for further development, the challenge, the fascination, are all there. Perhaps some day, one of you will make an important contribution to the world of mathematics.

THE HOW AND WHY WONDER BOOK OF
ELECTRICITY

By Jerome J. Notkin, Ed. D., Science Supervisor, Suffolk County, N. Y.
and Sidney Gulkin, M.S. in Ed., Teacher, New York City

Illustrated by Robert Patterson and Charles Bernard

Edited under the supervision of
   Dr. Paul E. Blackwood,
   Washington, D. C.

Text and illustrations approved by
   Oakes A. White, Brooklyn Children's Museum, Brooklyn, New York

GROSSET & DUNLAP • **Publishers** • **NEW YORK**

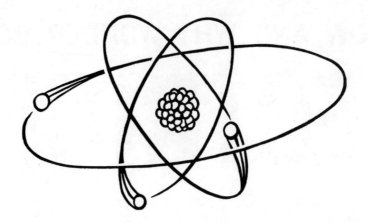

INTRODUCTION

When a town stands still for eight hours, it is missing something mighty important. One such town stood still because the electricity stopped. This was most inconvenient for everyone, but it did make a boy named Mike and his sister Susan Jane think about it. They were filled with questions: What is electricity? How do we make electricity? How does electricity get to our town?

Just as Mike and his sister explore the wonders of electricity with their father, so will inquisitive children everywhere get answers to their questions about electricity as they read this book. Like the others in the *How and Why Wonder Book* series, this science book is authentic and colorful and can be read with interest by the whole family.

The answers to questions about electricity that are now easy to give young people are the answers which stretched the minds of the greatest scientists less than a hundred years ago. Fortunately, books give children the wealth of information which took so long for scientists to discover.

Thinking, investigating and experimenting are the special paths which are basic to science. This book, which includes more than a dozen experiments to help readers discover what others have found before, will lead children along these same paths. It is an excellent addition to the school or home collection of science books for young readers and their parents.

Paul E. Blackwood

Dr. Blackwood is a professional employee in the U. S. Office of Education. This book was edited by him in his private capacity and no official support or endorsement by the Office of Education is intended or should be inferred.

Library of Congress Catalog Card Number: 61-1578

© 1960, by Wonder Books, Inc.   Special material © 1960, by Wonder Books, Inc.
All rights reserved under International and Pan-American Copyright Conventions.
Published simultaneously in Canada.   Printed in the United States of America.

CONTENTS

THE DAY THE TOWN STOOD STILL

Why is the main electrical cable the lifeline of a modern industrial town?

THIS story is not made up. It is true. It really happened. My town stood still for eight hours. Why? We had no electricity.

My house was not the same. The bells didn't ring. My mother's washing machine stopped dead. Our television set was dark and silent. The little radio in my room was just a box without a voice. Mother tried to use the telephone to order food. It was as silent as my radio. Our electric stove joined the washing machine, radio, telephone, and refrigerator. The electric clock in the kitchen was stopped at 10:36 A.M. That's when it happened. Mother changed the fuses. That was no help.

Our neighbor came running to us for help. Nothing was working in her house, either. She was really worried. Her baby's formula needed refrigeration. The food was becoming spoiled. She tried to call the doctor for her sick baby. But her phone was not working either.

My mother drove her in the car to pick up the doctor. When she arrived at the gas station to fill up the tank she was told that the pumps were not working. Several cars were stuck in the middle of the road. No gas!

Then mother turned the car radio on. It worked! It worked on the storage battery. The radio was full of news.

"Main cable at the power station destroyed by explosion. . . . Repairs are under way, but it will take at least eight hours. . . . Motorists are urged to give help to those who need it most."

So that was it! The main electrical cable had been damaged.

"Why is that cable so important?" I asked my mother.

"That cable is like the main pipe supplying us with water, Mike," my mother replied. "When that pipe is broken, the water stops running. There is just no other way of getting water. And there is no other way of getting electrical power until that cable is repaired."

How are we dependent upon electricity? By the time Dad came home it was dark. We helped him get into the house by flashlight. We had two candles — one in the kitchen, another in the living room.

We had our cold dinner by candlelight. My sister, Susan Jane, and I had a lot of fun, but Mother and Dad didn't think it was so funny.

The people on my street walked about with flashlights, knocking on each others' doors instead of ringing doorbells.

Everyone was excited.

"When will the lights go on?" people asked.

"Soon, soon," my Dad replied.

It seemed that a long time passed before the lights suddenly came on. The buzz of the refrigerator started. My little radio was on at full volume. The television set suddenly came to life with picture and sound.

It seemed as if the sun had suddenly begun to shine in the middle of the night.

My town began to move again!

5

WHAT IS THIS MAGICAL THING CALLED ELECTRICITY?

In what ways does a waterfall serve us?

"ELECTRICITY, or electrical power, just doesn't happen," said Dad. "It has to be made. How? What things are used to make it? Let's see.

"When my grandfather ground his wheat," said Dad, "he had to take it to a mill that was near a waterfall."

"Why near a waterfall?" I asked.

"Well, Mike," said Dad, "they used the waterfall for the power to run the mill. If you have never seen one, or don't know how it works, we can build a model. We need a cheese box, a stick for an axle or shaft, and some jar covers for blades.

"When water falls on these covers or blades, the shaft goes around, and it, in turn, moves wheels and gears. You see, then, that the fuel used to turn these wheels is free. The water moves the blades and the mill is in business."

"That's terrific, Dad, but how does falling water make electricity?" I asked.

THIS IS A HYDROELECTRIC DAM WHICH IS RUN BY WATER POWER OR THE FORCE OF FALLING WATER. WATER POWER MAY BE DESCRIBED AS THE POWER OF WATER USED TO MOVE OR DRIVE A MACHINE. THE MOVEMENT OR FLOW OF WATER IN RIVERS AND STREAMS BECOMES A SOURCE OF ENERGY. WHEN THE WATER, WHICH HAS BEEN COLLECTING BEHIND THE DAM, RUSHES DOWN, THE POWER OF ITS STRONG FLOW CAUSES THE GENERATOR TO TURN.

What are some of the ways we know of to make electricity?

"To make electricity which will not only turn a mill, but send out the electrons through roads made of wire, shafts have to be turned inside a tunnel, called a generator or dynamo. Water very often supplies the power to turn the shafts that make or generate this magical electricity."

"Oh, yes. We learned about some of these places in school. There is Hoover Dam, Niagara Falls, the Tennessee Valley Authority, Grand Coulee Dam, Roosevelt Dam and others like them throughout the country."

"Very good, Mike," smiled Dad. "And power from these places is sent hundreds of miles to homes, factories, farms and schools. It even runs railroads and subways."

"Really, Dad? Can water power do all that? But suppose there are no waterfalls or dams nearby?"

THERE ARE DIFFERENT KINDS OF POWER PLANTS, BUT THEY ALL HAVE SOMETHING IN COMMON. EACH POWER PLANT HAS A GENERATOR WHERE ELECTRICITY IS MADE. THIS IS A COAL-BURNING POWER PLANT. WATER IS HEATED BY A COAL FIRE AND STEAM MAKES THE GENERATOR MOVE.

What kind of power is used to run subways?

"The scientists and engineers have thought about that. They have figured out ways to make electricity from other things. Take coal as an example. That can help make electricity for use anywhere. Do you know that subways in many of our large cities run on coal-made electricity?"

"That's real magic!" said my sister, who had been listening quietly all along.

"No, Susan Jane, I wouldn't say it is magic. I like to call it science. That makes more sense. It can be explained and used by everyone, not only by magicians."

"Does it work like the dams?" Susan Jane asked.

"Something like it," Dad continued. "In the case of dams, water goes into a pipe where it turns the blades of the large wheels. When coal is used, steam goes into the pipes. The large wheels are called turbines."

TURBINE

GENERATOR

**What makes the
generator
spin around?**

"Is this turbine connected to anything?" I asked.

"Oh, yes. It's the turbine that makes the generator spin around. Electricity comes out the other side."

Susan Jane looked puzzled. She asked, "What is a generator? What does it do? How does it work?"

"I'll show you," said Dad. "We can make a model of a generator. But we'll need some things. Susan Jane, bring Mother's teakettle. Mike, bring your magnet and your flashlight. I have the other things we need."

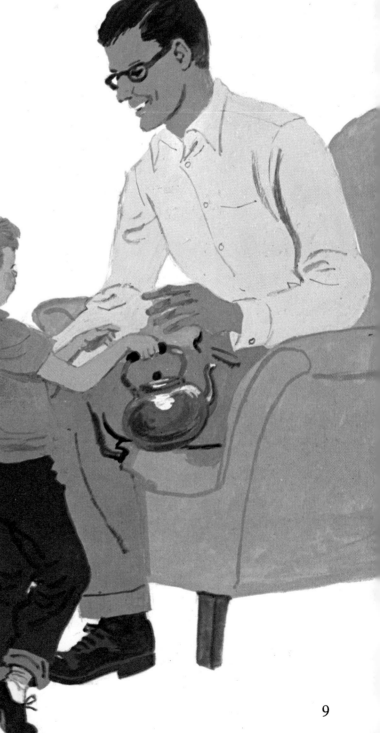

What part does the steam play in this experiment? Susan Jane and I ran to get these things, wondering how the kettle was going to be used.

"Now, then," said Dad when we returned, "watch and you will see how a generator makes electricity. The fire heats the water in the kettle. That makes the steam, just as burning coal can boil water to make steam. It is this steam power that pushes against the blades of the turbine. My turbine is made of cardboard, but it gives you the idea. Then the turbine turns the magnet inside a coil of electrical wire."

"Is a magnet really used?" I asked.

In what way are electrons pushed? "Yes. It is a magnet made by electricity, called an electromagnet. There are many turns of covered wire wound around an iron core. As the magnet moves inside a coil of wire, it pushes tiny things called electrons. When electrons are pushed or moved, electricity flows. That is why the light bulb that I removed from your flashlight goes on."

"Gosh, Dad, just think — a magnet and a wire make our television sets work!" I said.

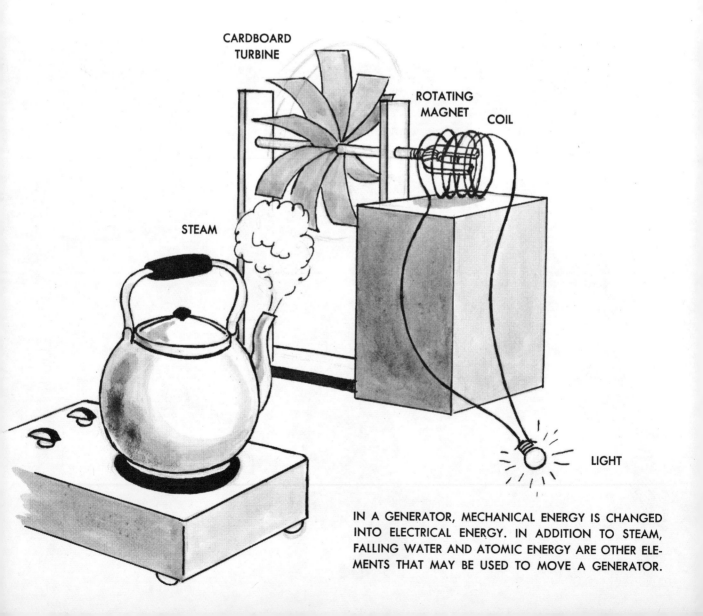

CARDBOARD TURBINE

ROTATING MAGNET

COIL

STEAM

LIGHT

IN A GENERATOR, MECHANICAL ENERGY IS CHANGED INTO ELECTRICAL ENERGY. IN ADDITION TO STEAM, FALLING WATER AND ATOMIC ENERGY ARE OTHER ELEMENTS THAT MAY BE USED TO MOVE A GENERATOR.

A BATTERY IN A FLASHLIGHT OR PORTABLE RADIO IS REALLY A KIND OF POWER STATION. SUCH BATTERIES ARE CALLED DRY CELLS. WE CALL THEM "DRY" BECAUSE THE WET ACID PASTE INSIDE A CELL IS SEALED UP TIGHT AND CANNOT SPILL OUT.

"Right, Mike. But remember, it is not this toy magnet and not this small piece of wire. It is a large electro-magnet turning inside a huge coil of wire. It looks more like a tunnel. The more wire in the coil, the more electrons can be moved. And we get more electricity.

Why is a cell called a portable power station? "Do you mean that my flashlight and portable radio carry a generator inside of them just for me, every time I want to use it?" I asked, looking at my flashlight.

"That's right. The battery is its own power station."

YOUR PORTABLE POWER STATION

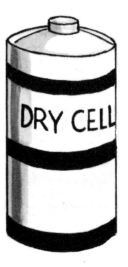

DRY CELL

POWER STATION

TRANSFORMER

HIGHWAYS THAT CARRY ELECTRICITY

How does a transformer help us get electricity to our homes?

"WHAT kind of pumps are used to push these electrons all the way from the power station to us?" I wanted to know.

"That's a good word — 'pumps.' I was coming to that. Do you know that as we ride along the highways there are electrical highways right above our heads that we hardly ever notice? Sometimes they are even under the roads."

"What are they for?" Susan Jane asked.

"They are the highways of wire where those invisible electrons are flowing toward homes, factories and farms," Dad answered. "As the generator makes the electricity, it has to be delivered where it is needed. Instead of trucks and trains that carry off goods from factories, wire or cables do the job here. They do it quietly, without any fuss."

"How do the wires do it?" asked my sister.

"Well, all along the roads where the electricity is carried are pumping stations called transformers. Right now, all I will say about them is that they help the electrons flow along.

SUB-STATION

TRANSFORMER

TRANSFORMERS

ELECTRICITY FROM THE POWER STATION IS CARRIED THROUGH WIRES TO HOMES, FAC-
TORIES, STORES, FARMS AND SCHOOLS. TRANSFORMERS HELP IN THE TRANSPORTATION
OF ELECTRICITY FROM THE POWER STATION TO ALL THESE PLACES. A TRANSFORMER IS
A MACHINE THAT TRANSFORMS OR CHANGES AN ELECTRIC CURRENT FROM A HIGH TO
A LOW VOLTAGE. IT CAN ALSO CHANGE CURRENT FROM A LOW TO A HIGH VOLTAGE.
THE TEXT AND ILLUSTRATIONS BEGINNING ON PAGE 19 WILL FURTHER EXPLAIN THE
FUNCTION OF A TRANSFORMER.

Why is copper most commonly used for electrical wiring?

"The wires or cables are made of material that must be a good conductor or carrier. It's like having a good clear road without bumps and rocks for cars to travel over. Good conductors are usually made of copper."

"Is copper the only conductor of electricity?" I asked.

"No. There are other ones. Silver is the best, but it's too expensive to use. Aluminum is also a good conductor and is gaining wider use because of its lightness. We use millions of tons of copper to make electrical wire for all purposes."

Why don't we use copper wires in our toaster?

"Do we always use copper?" Susan Jane wanted to know.

"No," said Dad. "Take our toaster, for example. The curled-up wires inside of it happen to be poor conductors."

"Wouldn't that mean that when electricity tries to get through, it will have a tough job?" I asked. I was puzzled.

Dad smiled. "What happens in a toaster? The wires get red hot. This shows us that electricity is having a difficult job passing through. But it makes our toast taste good. In an electric stove it broils our steaks and chops and cooks our meals. That's not all. Mother's electric iron uses these poor conductors or carriers, too. Otherwise the flat bottom of the iron would not get hot enough to iron our shirts, tablecloths and other things.

Can you name three electrical things in your home that use poor conductors?

"There are many other uses for these poor conductors. Can you name some other appliances which might have them?"

"Heating pads."

"Coffee makers."

"Waffle irons."

"An electric heater."

"An electric frying pan."

"That's enough," laughed Dad. "Now let's ask Mother to put electricity to work and prepare some lunch. This talk about steak and chops is making me hungry."

"Me, too," we echoed, and everyone went into the kitchen.

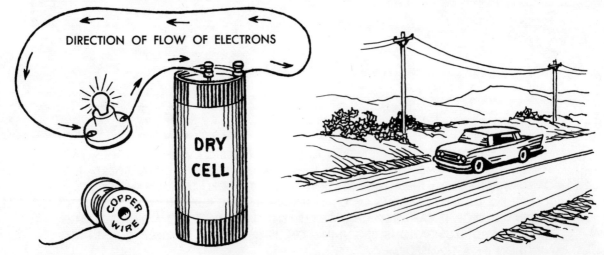

DIRECTION OF FLOW OF ELECTRONS

DRY CELL

COPPER WIRE

COPPER IS ONE OF THE BEST CONDUCTORS OF ELECTRIC CURRENT, AND IT IS USED WIDELY IN THE MANUFACTURE OF THIN ELECTRICAL WIRE, AS WELL AS THE HEAVIER CABLES ALONG HIGHWAYS.

ELECTRICITY IS REALLY A FIRST COUSIN OF MAGNETS

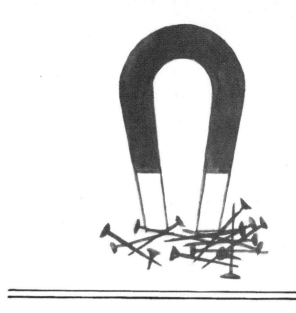

Are magnets and electricity related?

"YOU know, Dad, one of the things that you said yesterday still confuses me. What does the electrical magnet have to do with making electricity? I know that magnets have some kind of power. They can attract nails and pins and other things. But how do magnets help us make electricity?"

While I was talking, Susan Jane was picking things up with my magnet.

"Magnets and electricity are in the same family," explained Dad. "We might even say they are cousins. We can try something to clear this up."

MAGNETS HAVE A DRAWING OR PULLING POWER, AND ATTRACT THINGS MADE OF STEEL, IRON AND NICKEL.

THE WORD *MAGNETISM* COMES FROM THE NAME *MAGNESIA*, AN ANCIENT CITY OF ASIA, WHERE MANY LOADSTONES WERE FOUND. THE LOADSTONE, ALSO SPELLED LODE-STONE, IS A MAGNETIC ROCK, AND WAS USED BY ANCIENT PEOPLES IN THE SAILING OF SHIPS. LIKE A COMPASS NEEDLE, A PIECE OF LOADSTONE ROCK WILL POINT NORTH.

"Can we help?" begged Susan Jane.

"Why, sure. Mike, bring down your scout compass. Susan Jane, bring the cover of your crayon box."

When we returned, Dad had removed the dry cell from my flashlight.

"Put the compass into the cover," Dad instructed. "Wind some insulated wire about eight or ten times around the cover."

What happens when electricity flows through a wire?

Then Dad touched one end of the wire, which had been stripped back, to the bottom of the dry cell, and he touched the other end to the center part at the top of the cell.

"Did you see what happened?" asked Dad.

"Yes, the needle of Mike's compass moved."

"That's right. You know that one magnet can move another magnet. When electricity went through the wire, the needle, which is a magnet, moved. That means that, somewhere, there was another magnet. When electricity flows through wires, there is magnetism around the wires."

"Can we see it?" asked Susan Jane.

"No. Not any more than we can see magnetism pulling nails to Mike's magnet. But the magnetism is there, all right."

"I'm not sure I understand," I said.

HANS CHRISTIAN OERSTED DISCOVERED THAT ELECTRICITY AND MAGNETISM WERE RELATED. IN THE YEAR 1820, OERSTED OBSERVED THAT WHEN HE SENT AN ELECTRIC CURRENT THROUGH A WIRE THAT WAS NEAR A COMPASS, THE COMPASS NEEDLE MOVED. HE SHOWED THAT THE FLOW OF ELECTRICITY THROUGH A WIRE CAUSES A MAGNETISM AROUND THE WIRE. MICHAEL FARADAY ALSO EXPERIMENTED WITH ELECTRICITY AND MAGNETISM. HIS IMPORTANT WORK RESULTED IN THE FIRST ELECTRIC GENERATOR.

What happens when a magnet moves inside a coil of wire?

"You will soon, Mike. If a magnet moves when electrons go through a coil, would electrons move when a magnet passes through a coil? This puzzled a scientist several hundred years ago, and he decided to experiment. His experiment worked, and that marked the beginning of many wonderful things.

"If we use a small magnet and a small wire, only a few electrons would move. But when we move very powerful magnets inside thousands of coils, many electrons flow. It doesn't matter whether the magnets or the coils move, but it's the movement which generates the electricity."

"I understand it more clearly now, Dad."

"Good. As you see, there's nothing magical about it," said Dad. "But let's back up a bit. Do you remember that I kept tapping one end of the wire to the dry cell to make the compass move? We can do it easier if we use a switch, such as we have in our house."

"Does it make any difference if it's an up-and-down switch or one that we use to ring the doorbell?" asked Susan Jane.

How is a switch like a door?

"Not one bit," answered Dad. "Each one can turn something on and off. When we close any switch, the connection is completed and the electrons can flow again. When we open the switch, the connection is broken and the electrons cannot flow."

Susan Jane exclaimed, "That's just like opening or closing a gate or door."

"Of course! That's a nice way to put it," complimented Dad. "Did you ever hear the expression, 'completing the circuit' or 'breaking the circuit'? That's what is meant. When the switch is closed, the light, the refrigerator, the waffle iron, the coffee maker, and your electric train, all go on. When we turn the switch off, these appliances go off."

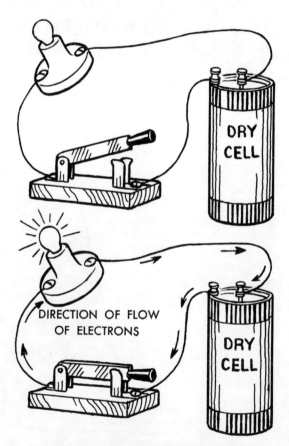

DIRECTION OF FLOW OF ELECTRONS

TOP: BREAKING THE CIRCUIT.
BOTTOM: COMPLETING THE CIRCUIT.

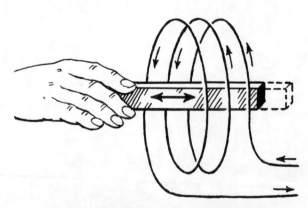

THE MOVEMENT OF A MAGNET INSIDE A COIL OF WIRE GENERATES ELECTRICITY.

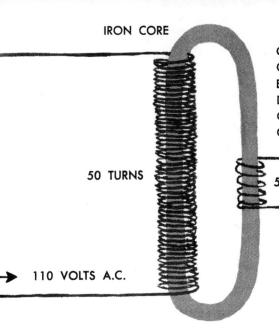

IRON CORE

50 TURNS

110 VOLTS A.C. →

5 TURNS

OUR HOMES ARE OFTEN SUPPLIED WITH 110 VOLTS OF ELECTRICITY, BUT TOY ELECTRIC TRAINS, FOR EXAMPLE, NEED FEWER VOLTS TO OPERATE. STEP-DOWN TRANSFORMERS STEP DOWN, OR DECREASE, THE VOLTAGE OF AN ALTERNATING CURRENT, ENABLING A TOY TRAIN TO RUN.

11 VOLTS A.C.
TO RUN TOY TRAIN →

ELECTRICITY NEEDS PUMPING STATIONS

Why is your toy train transformer called a step-down transformer?

"DOESN'T the train set you gave me for my birthday work from my transformer? I never really knew what that word meant," I said.

"Let's look it up in the dictionary," suggested Susan Jane.

"A good idea," said Dad. "Let's see. Transform means, 'to change in form.'

"When we use a transformer for a train, we plug it into the wall socket. Our home is supplied with 110 volts of electricity. Our train uses much less, perhaps eight to twelve volts. How can we cut it down?"

"Does the transformer do the job for us?" I wanted to know.

"Yes, it does. It steps it down, just as it does in other parts of the house. We have a transformer to step down the voltage before it goes into our doorbell. We could use batteries, too, but we'd have to replace them when they were used up."

"What does the inside of a transformer look like?" Susan Jane asked.

"I can sketch it roughly for you," said Dad. "Very simply it works like this. There are two coils of wire, one larger than the other. If current is sent through the first coil, magnetism surrounds it. The second coil is affected by the magnetism and electricity comes out of its wires.

"If the second coil is larger than the first coil, more electricity comes out than went into the original coil. If the second coil is smaller, as in your train set, less voltage comes out.

"So we can say that the transformer is used to raise or lower the voltage of the current. We can step it up or step it down.

"Remember, when we speak of current, we mean A.C. or alternating current. Dry cells and storage batteries are all D.C. or direct current."

"Are these transformers used only in toy trains and in doorbells?" inquired Susan Jane.

"No. Their most important use is in transporting electricity from the power station to places many miles away.

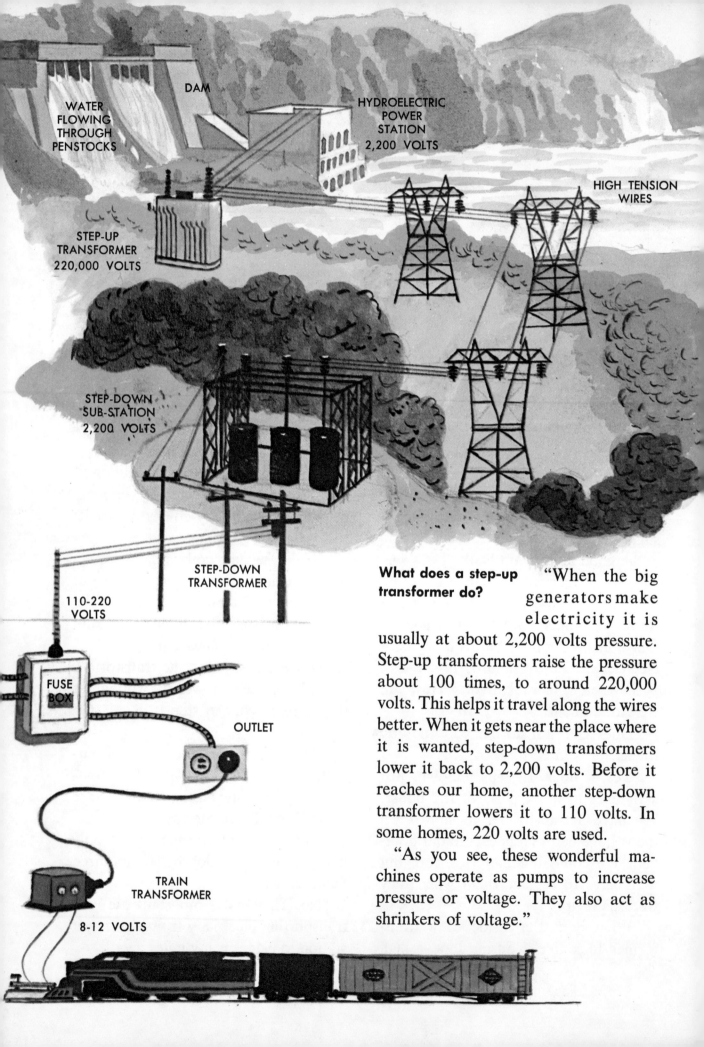

DAM

WATER
FLOWING
THROUGH
PENSTOCKS

HYDROELECTRIC
POWER
STATION
2,200 VOLTS

HIGH TENSION
WIRES

STEP-UP
TRANSFORMER
220,000 VOLTS

STEP-DOWN
SUB-STATION
2,200 VOLTS

STEP-DOWN
TRANSFORMER

110-220
VOLTS

FUSE
BOX

OUTLET

TRAIN
TRANSFORMER

8-12 VOLTS

What does a step-up transformer do?

"When the big generators make electricity it is usually at about 2,200 volts pressure. Step-up transformers raise the pressure about 100 times, to around 220,000 volts. This helps it travel along the wires better. When it gets near the place where it is wanted, step-down transformers lower it back to 2,200 volts. Before it reaches our home, another step-down transformer lowers it to 110 volts. In some homes, 220 volts are used.

"As you see, these wonderful machines operate as pumps to increase pressure or voltage. They also act as shrinkers of voltage."

WE MUST OBSERVE SAFETY RULES

"DO YOU remember when I had my arm in a sling? That was a very bad burn I received as a result of carelessness with electricity," Dad told us.

"How did it happen?" Susan Jane wanted to know.

"I tried to plug in my electric razor while my hands were wet," Dad explained. "I am pretty lucky to be alive.

I was so badly burned that the doctor had to treat me for several weeks before I could use my hand.

Can you remember at least five "never" rules?

"If you really want to have fun with electricity," said Dad, "you must first learn to play the important game of NEVER."

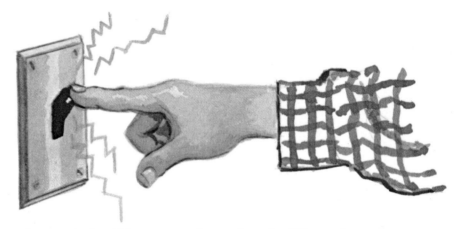

NEVER touch a switch with wet or damp hands. Water is a conductor. You might be badly burned or receive a severe shock. When you touch a switch, or any electric appliance, be sure your hands are dry.

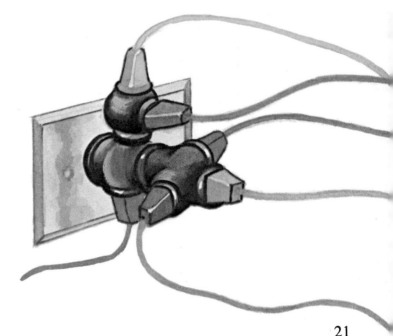

NEVER overload your connections. Don't try to plug too many electric appliances into one home appliance circuit. It is dangerous and can cause a short circuit or fire.

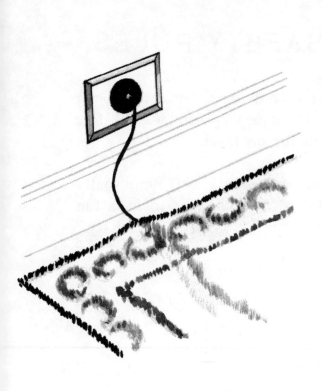

NEVER put electrical wires under carpets and rugs.

NEVER put a penny in the fuse box. Use the proper-sized fuse.

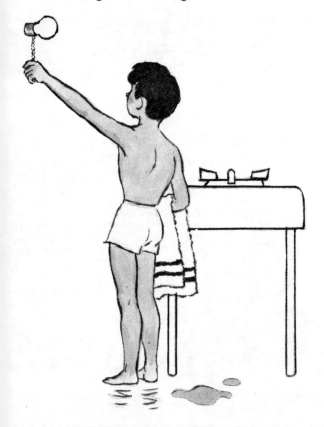

NEVER pull the chain of a light bulb if you are standing on a wet floor.

NEVER poke around the radio or television set if the switch is on.

NEVER touch an electrical appliance, switch, radio, or television set while bathing or when wet.

NEVER remain under or near a tree during an electrical storm or thunderstorm. Lightning may strike it.

NEVER remain in a lake during a thunderstorm.

NEVER, but never, touch a broken cable after or during a storm, or at any time. Call a policeman or fireman.

NEVER place anything except a plug into a wall socket.

"Remember," continued Dad as we listened very carefully, "electricity can be your friend or your enemy. You cannot argue with it. It will not forgive your mistakes. It will not accept your apology. It will reward you or punish you. It does not play favorites. Treat it with respect and understanding and it will serve you loyally."

DRY CELLS ARE THE SAFE WAY

DAD walked over to us and placed his hands on our shoulders. "Well, if you follow these NEVER rules, you will be doing the right thing. You can still have lots of fun with electricity if you work with dry cells. They cost little and you can carry them with you. You can put them in a box and take them to school, to the playground, to your friend's home or porch, and perform experiments. You can have a grand time. They are useful and safe."

Why should we never place a piece of metal across the two terminals? "Are there any NEVER rules for dry cells?" I asked.

"Only one," said Dad. "NEVER put a piece of metal across the terminals. If you do, you will cause a short circuit and burn out the dry cell. Take care of these little power stations."

Dad opened my flashlight and removed the small dry cells. He gave one to my sister and one to me.

In how many ways can we use dry cells? "This fine invention is very useful to many people. What a help it is for those who have to walk in places where lighting a match or candle would be dangerous!

"When the farmer has to attend to his livestock in the barn, a match or candle could be very dangerous."

"That's right," said Susan Jane. "One slip and the whole barn could be set on fire."

"What about the coal miner who has to go poking around in the dark?" I suggested. "There are gases there that could cause an explosion if he lit a match."

"You are both right," said Dad. "And don't forget how Doctor Ross uses his flashlight to look at your throats. He carries it in his pocket like a fountain pen. The dry cell is used now more than ever before."

"How does a dry cell work?" I asked.

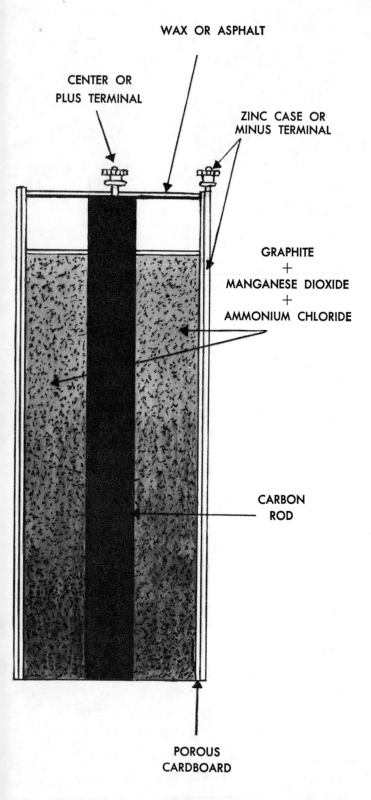

WAX OR ASPHALT

CENTER OR
PLUS TERMINAL

ZINC CASE OR
MINUS TERMINAL

GRAPHITE
+
MANGANESE DIOXIDE
+
AMMONIUM CHLORIDE

CARBON
ROD

POROUS
CARDBOARD

DIAGRAM OF A DRY CELL

"If you were to look inside one, you would see chemicals. They are ready to work — quietly and efficiently — to serve you when you press a button or flip a switch. There are no secret words to say to make it work. Anyone can learn how to do it. It's easy and it's fun. In fact, you can teach it to your friends.

Can you name some of the parts of a dry cell?

"Just as a magnet has two poles, north and south, so a dry cell has two poles, plus and minus. Do you see the center rod? That's made of carbon — the plus side. The case around the cell is usually made of a metal called zinc. That is the minus pole."

Why is it called a dry cell?

Dad took his hacksaw and cut a dry cell down the center.

"Now we are coming to the chemical plant that manufactures the electrical energy we sometimes call electrons. It's made into a hard paste so that it can be carried about. That's one of the reasons these cells are called 'dry cells.' "

Why is a storage battery called a "battery" and not a "cell"?

"Does our car use the same kind of battery or dry cell?" I asked.

"It is a battery, but not a dry cell," answered Dad. "The car battery is called a storage battery. It does not use a hard paste like your flashlight cell. We may call it a wet battery."

"A wet battery?" Susan Jane echoed.

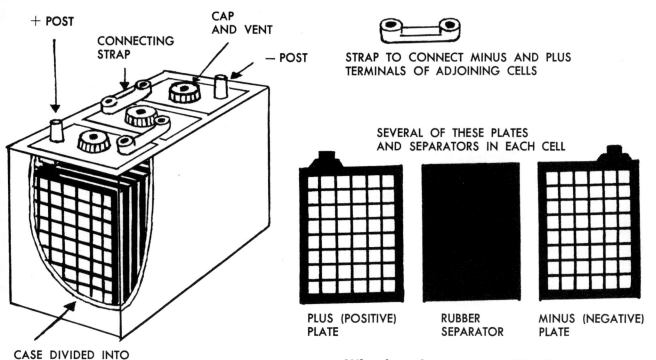

+ POST

CONNECTING STRAP

CAP AND VENT

— POST

STRAP TO CONNECT MINUS AND PLUS TERMINALS OF ADJOINING CELLS

SEVERAL OF THESE PLATES AND SEPARATORS IN EACH CELL

PLUS (POSITIVE) PLATE

RUBBER SEPARATOR

MINUS (NEGATIVE) PLATE

CASE DIVIDED INTO 3 COMPARTMENTS OR CELLS

DIAGRAM OF A STORAGE BATTERY

What are the two liquids used in a storage battery?

"Right. It uses distilled water and an acid — a very dangerous acid."

"Do you mean that our car battery also makes electrons like a chemical plant?" I asked.

"A chemical plant is correct," smiled Dad. "The storage battery in our car is a real power station. It starts our motor and helps it run. It makes our light go on. It wipes the windows in a rainstorm. It runs our heater in the winter. It gives our radio power. My cigarette lighter uses the battery. Even the windows open and close in my new car, thanks to the battery."

"Why do we use distilled water? Is it cleaner?" I wanted to know.

"Why do we need acid, if it's so dangerous?" asked Susan Jane.

Why does the storage battery use distilled water?

"Distilled water, like rain water, does not have any impurities," said Dad. "And the acid combines with the lead to give us electricity. The car uses the battery to spark the gasoline in the motor to get it started. Without it the car wouldn't move."

Dad motioned for us to come over to his car. He raised the hood and we peered in to see the battery. "The storage battery in the car is not as safe to touch as the dry cell in your flashlight, Mike. The acid can cause a severe burn and make holes in our clothing.

"Do you remember the NEVER game?" Dad asked us.

"We sure do," answered my sister.

"Good. NEVER touch any part of the battery when the motor is on."

Mother walked over to us. "How would you junior scientists like to climb into this chemical or electrical or gasoline-operated machine and take a ride with me? I'll need some help with the groceries," she said.

THE POLICEMAN OF THE HIGHWAYS

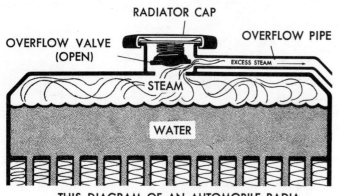

RADIATOR CAP

OVERFLOW VALVE (OPEN)

OVERFLOW PIPE

EXCESS STEAM

STEAM

WATER

THIS DIAGRAM OF AN AUTOMOBILE RADIA-
TOR SHOWS AN OPEN OVERFLOW VALVE,
ALLOWING EXCESS STEAM TO ESCAPE. SUCH
A VALVE IS NEEDED IN ORDER TO RELIEVE
STEAM PRESSURE.

How does the overflow valve in the automobile protect it?

THERE were many cars on the road to the supermarket, and a policeman was on duty directing traffic. Every so often he would stop the cars from moving until the traffic ahead cleared up.

"Why can't he let us go through?" I asked.

"The officer is looking out for our safety," Mother explained.

"He is like a safety valve," said Dad, "just as we have safety valves in locomotives and in the radiator of this car. These valves are seldom used, but they are very important. They are the policemen of these machines. When the locomotive has worked up too much steam and is in danger of exploding, the safety valve releases the extra steam. The same thing happens in the radiator of the car."

The policeman signaled us to go ahead.

ONE WAY

Why is the fuse often called the twenty-four-hour policeman?

"Just as the policeman stops traffic to make sure that the cars don't crash into one another, so a fuse in our home stops electrons from overcrowding. For when too many lines are plugged into one outlet, the electrons, like the cars, begin crashing into each other. When that happens, the extra movement makes the wires warm. The wires may get so hot that the walls of the house could catch fire.

"The fuse stops these electrons just as they begin to get hot. 'Stop,' says the policeman. 'Blow,' says the fuse. The lights go out. The toaster stops toasting and the broiler stops broiling."

"Too many electrical appliances were on at one time. They overloaded the circuit. That was one of the NEVER rules," I said.

"Very good, Mike. You learned quickly. It was a good thing that the fuse was there. Remember that the little fuse box is our policeman. It is guarding our home and our lives. I'll show you how to make a fuse later on," said Dad. "In fact, I'll write down the directions for other activities which you can do to learn a lot more about electricity."

Here are the activities that Susan Jane's and Mike's Dad suggested. You can try them, too.

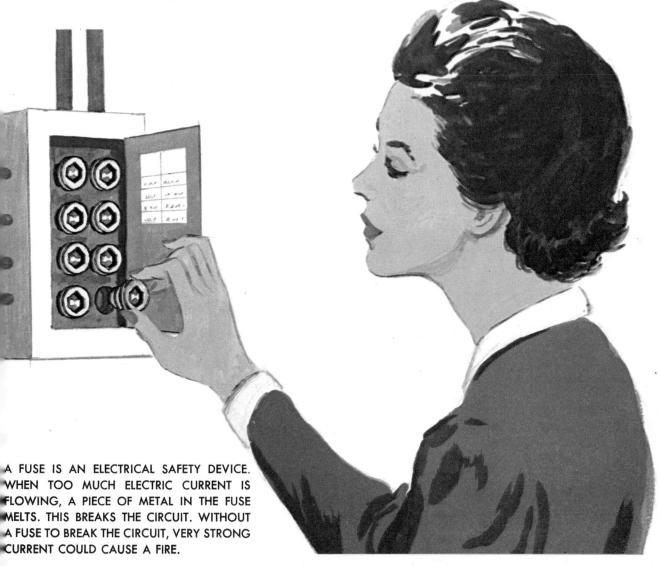

A FUSE IS AN ELECTRICAL SAFETY DEVICE. WHEN TOO MUCH ELECTRIC CURRENT IS FLOWING, A PIECE OF METAL IN THE FUSE MELTS. THIS BREAKS THE CIRCUIT. WITHOUT A FUSE TO BREAK THE CIRCUIT, VERY STRONG CURRENT COULD CAUSE A FIRE.

ACTIVITIES FOR JUNIOR ELECTRICIANS

TRY these activities. Don't worry if you are not too successful at first. Follow the directions and diagrams as carefully as you can. You will have a great deal of fun.

Remember: When you see the word "wire" it means insulated wire. When it says, "connect wire," it means that the ends of the wire are to be stripped of insulation, material or paint.

NO. 1. HOW DOES YOUR FLASHLIGHT WORK?

You will use:
Flashlight
Piece of wire

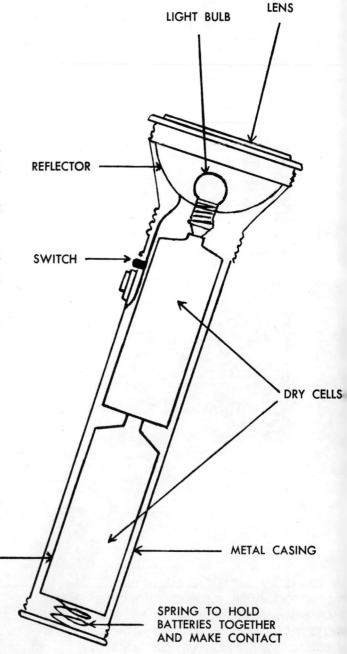

LIGHT BULB

LENS

REFLECTOR

SWITCH

DRY CELLS

ZINC CONTAINER

METAL CASING

SPRING TO HOLD BATTERIES TOGETHER AND MAKE CONTACT

Do this:

Turn your flashlight on and then off. Now that you are sure the flashlight works, take it apart to see the different parts.

Strip the insulation from both ends of a piece of wire about six inches long.

Wrap one end of the bare wire around the base of the bulb that you removed from the flashlight.

Touch the bottom of the bulb to the center terminal of the cell.

Touch the end of the wire to the bottom of the cell.

The light goes on.

Why it works:

When you closed the switch of the flashlight, you completed a circuit. That is, you provided a closed path for the current to follow in a circle.

You will use:
- Dry cell (large or small)
- Flashlight bulb
- Miniature socket
- Wire
- Piece of metal
- Block of wood
- Two nails
- Hammer

Do this:

Do you remember *Activity No. 1?* We were able to turn the light on by touching the wire to the cell.

Then we removed the wire and the light went out.

That's pretty simple. But an easier way is to use a switch.

Take a piece of metal — four inches long, and one inch wide. (You can cut it from a tin can if you are careful.)

Nail one end of it on the block of wood.

Place another nail in the wood under the other end of the metal.

Do not place either nail all the way down in the wood.

Be sure that the loose end of the metal is not resting on the nail beneath.

Now you have a switch.

Connect one wire from either terminal of the dry cell to the nail under the metal.

Remember to strip off the insulation from the ends of all the wires you use.

Connect a second wire from the other terminal of the dry cell to either terminal of the miniature socket.

Connect a third wire from the other terminal of the socket to the nail hold-ing the strip of metal in place.

Now press the switch.

If you have made all the connections properly, the circuit is closed and the light will go on.

Save this switch. You will use it many times in these activities.

Why it works:

If you have a large dry cell, you will notice two terminals at the top. Connecting wires to them is done much more easily than with the small flashlight cell.

But all of these activities can be done with either cell, except that the large cell lasts longer and it is easier to use.

Each cell gives us 1½ volts.

Connect the wires the way you did in *Activity No. 1.*

The switch is a convenient way for us to open and close a circuit. It is easier than connecting and disconnecting wires. It is also a safer way to turn the lights and other electrical appliances on and off.

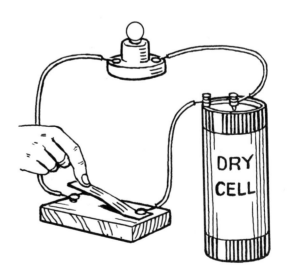

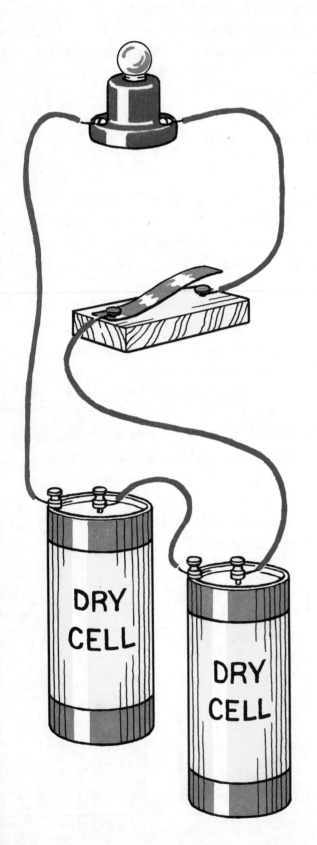

You will use:
Two dry cells
Wire
Switch
Flashlight bulb
Miniature socket

Do this:

Do you remember how bright the bulb was in *Activity No. 2?* Now let's see what happens when we add another dry cell to the circuit. Of course, it has to be connected properly.

Connect one wire between the center terminal of cell 1 and the end terminal of cell 2.

The remainder of the connections are similar to the way you did them in the previous activity.

One wire is connected between the terminal of cell 2 and a socket terminal.

Another wire goes from the other socket terminal to either nail in the switch.

The last wire goes between the other nail of the switch and back to cell 1.

Press the switch.

See how much brighter the light bulb is?

Why it works:

The two dry cells connected in series resulted in about twice the power of one cell.

This made the bulb brighter.

When you connected two cells of 1½ volts each in series, you really added them.

How many volts do you have now?

Would you like to try it with an electric bell?

NO. 4. HOW CAN WE CONNECT TWO DRY CELLS TO MAKE THEM LAST LONGER?

You will use:
Two dry cells
Wire
Switch
Flashlight bulb
Miniature socket

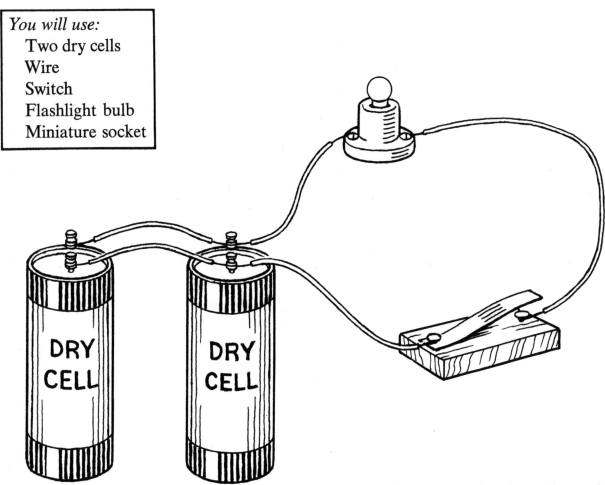

Do this:

Connect the dry cells, wires, switch and bulb as shown in the illustration.

First connect one dry cell in a circuit with your switch and the light bulb.

If you have forgotten how to do it, go back to *Activity No. 2.*

Now connect two other wires to the terminals on cell 2.

Take the wire from the center terminal of cell 2 and connect it to the center terminal of cell 1.

Take the wire coming from the end terminal of cell 2 and connect it to the end terminal of cell 1.

You should now have two wires connected to each of the terminals of cell 1.

Press the switch.

Notice that the light is not any brighter than it was when only one cell was in the circuit.

Why it works:

You connected the two dry cells in parallel.

No, the light is not brighter than it was with one dry cell.

That is why parallel connections are better when cells are to be used over a long period of time.

33

NO. 5. HOW CAN WE CONNECT SEVERAL LIGHT BULBS IN SERIES?

You will use:
  Dry cell
  Wire
  Switch
  Two flashlight bulbs
  Two miniature sockets

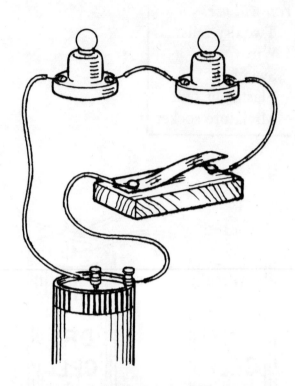

Do this:

Connect one wire from one terminal of your dry cell to one terminal of the switch.

Now connect a second wire from the other terminal of the dry cell to one terminal of socket 1.

Connect a third wire between the remaining terminal of socket 1 to one terminal of socket 2.

Now connect a fourth wire between the remaining terminal of socket 2 to the last terminal of the switch.

Close the switch. The bulbs should light.

Each bulb is not as bright as it was when we used one in our circuit.

Now unscrew one bulb. The other bulb will go out.

Why it works:

When both bulbs were lit, electricity was flowing in a complete path through the circuit. It was able to flow out of the dry cell right through the bulbs and return to the dry cell — like a merry-go-round.

This is called connecting bulbs in series.

In *Activity No. 2* we used one dry cell having 1½ volts to light one bulb. The little bulb was bright.

Now we divided that 1½ volts between two bulbs in series. Each bulb received only ¾ of a volt.

Do you see why the bulbs in series were a bit dim?

When you unscrewed one bulb, the other one went out.

Do you know why?

Because you interrupted the circuit. The electrons were not flowing in a merry-go-round.

Oh, yes, did you know that the tiny wire in the little bulb you removed was part of the path through which the electrons flow?

It's a good thing our homes are wired in parallel.

Can you imagine what a hard job it would be to find out which bulb was burned out if they were connected in series?

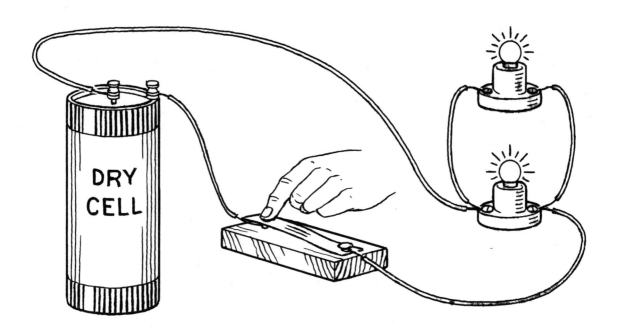

NO. 6. HOW CAN WE CONNECT SEVERAL LIGHT BULBS IN PARALLEL?

You will use:
  Dry cell
  Wire
  Switch
  Two flashlight bulbs
  Two miniature sockets

Do this:

Connect your dry cell, switch and one socket in a complete circuit.

Press the switch. See how bright it is? Try to remember how it looks.

Now we are going to bring another bulb into our circuit.

In *Activity No. 5* we connected them in series.

Do you remember the disadvantages of that circuit?

Connect a wire between one terminal of socket 1, already in the circuit, to one terminal of socket 2.

Now connect another wire between the other terminals of sockets 1 and 2. Notice that there are two wires coming out of each terminal of socket 1.

Press the switch. Both bulbs should light.

Are you surprised to find that each bulb is just as bright as the single bulb you lit at the start of this activity?

Now unscrew one bulb. The other one remains lit.

More surprises!

Why it works:

You have connected two bulbs in parallel.

Each bulb has its own path to and from the dry cell.

The path does not have to go through both bulbs as it did in a series circuit.

Try tracing the path of the electric current to each bulb.

Since each bulb is connected directly to the dry cell, each is as bright as if you had only one bulb.

Now if one bulb goes out, the other remains lit, as in your own house.

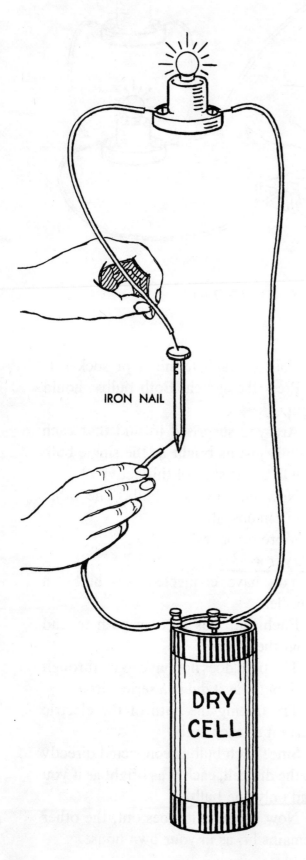

IRON NAIL

DRY CELL

You will use:
Dry cell
Wire
Flashlight bulb
Miniature socket

Do this:

Connect a wire between one terminal of a dry cell and one terminal of a light socket. Attach one end of another wire to the other dry cell terminal.

Attach a third wire to the other terminal of the socket.

The ends of the two wires should be free.

Touch the two free ends of the wire together briefly.

You have now completed the circuit and the light should go on.

Touch the two free ends of the wires to opposite ends of an iron nail. The light will go on.

Test other materials in this manner to see which ones help the light go on.

Why it works:

Until now we have used wires to complete our circuits. We saw how a nail acted in the same way.

As you see, some metals are good conductors of electricity. Some are better than others.

If you test glass, wood, plastic, or rubber, you will find that the light will not go on. Not enough electricity passes through them to light the bulb.

These materials are called non-conductors.

NO. 8. HOW CAN WE MAKE A QUIZ BOARD?

You will use:
Dry cell
Wire
Flashlight bulb
Miniature socket
Cardboard
Nail

Do this:

Use the nail to punch six holes down the left side of a piece of cardboard, and six holes down the right side.

Place the end of one wire in any hole at the left and the other end in any hole at the right.

Strip the insulation from the ends of the wire and secure it in place.

Repeat this with five other wires.

You now have six wires in place in a haphazard way.

Set this aside for a while.

Connect a wire between a dry cell terminal and a socket terminal.

Connect another wire to the remaining terminal of the dry cell.

Now attach a third wire to the remaining terminal of the socket.

This is similar to your conductor tester in *Activity No. 7*.

Touch the two free ends of the wires together briefly. The light will go on.

Hold the cardboard so that you cannot see how the wires are connected.

Place the name of a baseball player on the left side, which will serve as the question, and the name of his team on the right side, which will be the answer.

Be sure that the player and team are on opposite ends of the same wire.

Ask your friend to take the two free ends of the wires from the cell and socket. Now try to touch the matching questions and answers.

Why it works:

By touching the question with one end of the wire, and the answer with the other end of the wire, the light will go on. This happens because the circuit has been completed.

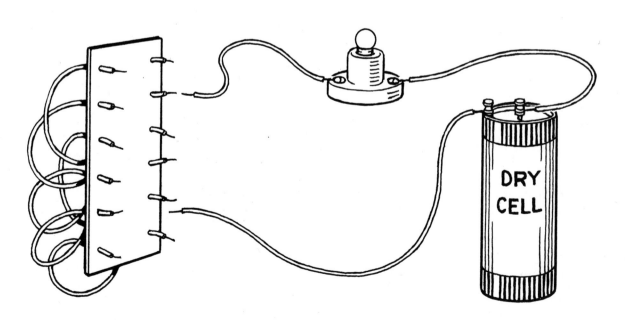

NO. 9. HOW DOES A FUSE PROTECT US?

You will use:
Dry cell
Wire
Flashlight bulb
Miniature socket
Tin foil
Block of wood
Two thumbtacks

Do this:

Cut a piece of tin foil so that the center is as thin as a piece of wire.

Secure it to a block of wood with two thumbtacks. Do not push the tacks all the way down. Set this aside for a while.

Strip about two inches of insulation away from the middle portion of two wires. Connect these wires to the two terminals of a miniature socket.

Connect the other end of one of these wires to a dry cell terminal.

Connect the other end of the second wire to one of the thumbtacks of your fuse board.

Be sure that the stripped end of the wire is in contact with the metal of the tack.

Connect a third wire between the remaining dry cell terminal and the remaining thumbtack.

The light should go on.

Lay a bare wire or any piece of metal across the two bare wires. The light will go out.

Did you see how the tin-foil fuse melted at the narrow part?

Why it works:

The light went on because the circuit was complete. Electricity flowed through the tin-foil fuse, as it does in our homes.

When you placed a piece of metal across the two bared wires, you caused a short circuit. Electricity was able to flow back to the dry cell without passing through the bulb to light it.

The electricity that was not used by the bulb caused the wires to become hotter. The tin-foil strip melts at a lower temperature than the other wires. When this happened, the circuit was broken and no more electricity flowed.

The fuse protects us by burning out. If the fuse were not there, the wires would have become hotter and hotter. This could have resulted in a fire.

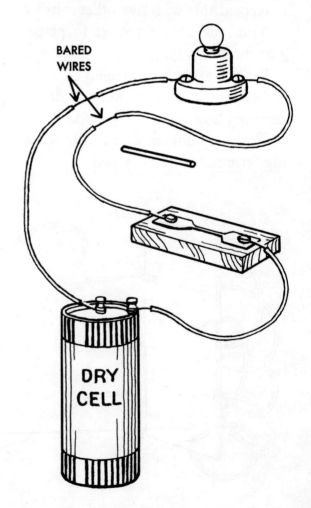

BARED WIRES

DRY CELL

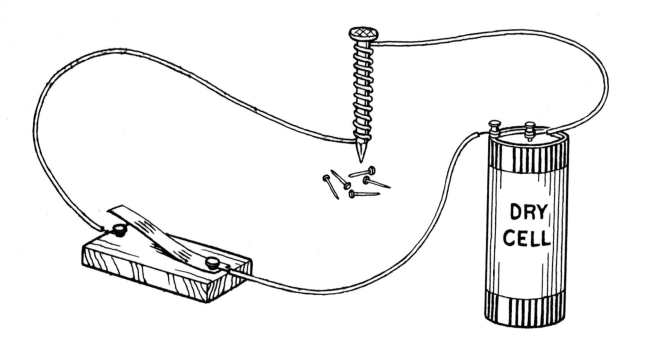

NO. 10. HOW CAN WE MAKE AN ELECTROMAGNET?

You will use:
 Dry cell
 Wire
 Switch
 Large nail
 Small nails or paper clips

Do this:

Wind about ten turns of wire around a large nail.

Strip the insulation from the ends of the wire.

Connect one end of the wire to one terminal of a dry cell and the other end to the terminal of the switch.

Prepare a second wire. Connect this wire to the other terminal of the dry cell and the other end to the switch.

Now close the switch and try to pick up paper clips or small nails with the large nail.

Open the switch and the small nails, or the paper clips, will fall down.

Why it works:

The electricity from one part of the dry cell flows through the many turns of wire back into the dry cell.

When electricity flows through a wire, the wire has magnetic power around it. If the wire happens to be in the form of a coil, the magnetism is even stronger.

Now, when we put an iron nail inside the coil, the nail becomes a magnet. This is true only for as long as the electricity is flowing in the circuit. It is a magnet when you want it to be.

Do you see how magnets and electricity are related?

Our magnet really depends on the electricity it gets from the dry cell.

We find electromagnets all around us.

We find them in refrigerators, in television sets, telephones, in Dad's electric shaver and in Mother's vacuum cleaner.

NO. 11. HOW CAN WE MAKE AN ELECTROMAGNET STRONGER?

You will use:
Dry cell
Wire
Switch
Large nail
Small nails

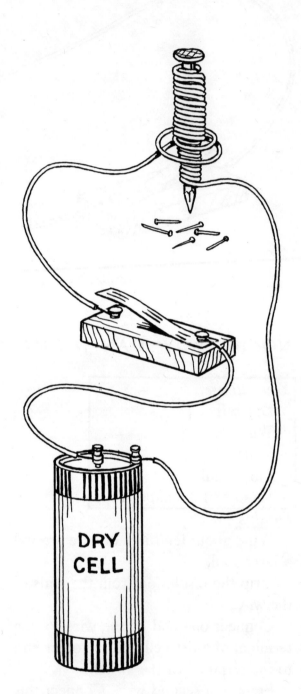

Do this:

Connect your electromagnet in the same way that you did in *Activity No. 10* — except for one thing. This time wind *twenty-five* turns of wire around the large nail.

Close the switch. See how many small nails you can pick up.

Do this two more times.

Do you know how to find the average number of nails picked up?

Add the number of nails picked up in three tries. Then divide by three.

This will give you the average number of nails picked up by the electromagnet with the twenty-five turns of wire.

Write the average down.

Now that you are an expert, wrap twenty-five more turns of wire around the nail, making fifty turns all together.

Count the number of nails you can pick up this time. Do this two more times.

Find the average number of nails picked up by your electromagnet with fifty turns of wire. Write this down.

Compare the two averages. You will see that more nails were picked up by the electromagnet with more turns.

Why it works:

The more turns of wire you have, the more magnetism there is around the coil, and the stronger the electromagnet.

You may have found that you picked up about twice as many nails when you doubled the number of turns.

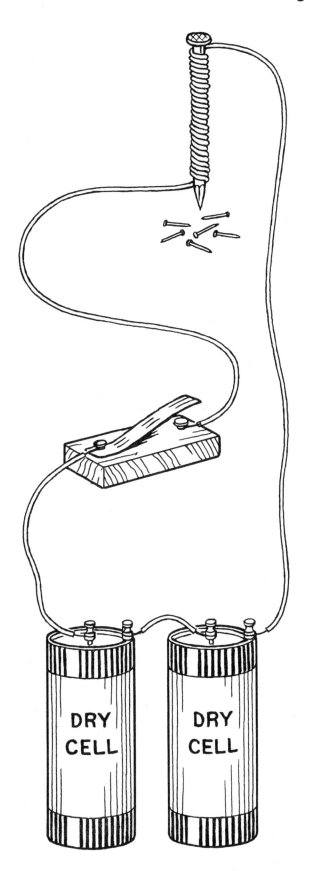

You will use:
    Two dry cells
    Wire
    Switch
    Large nail
    Small nails

Do this:

Do you remember how to connect two dry cells in series to give us more electricity?

You must remember to connect one wire between the plus or center terminal of one dry cell to the minus or end terminal of the other cell.

Connect a second wire from the other terminal of one cell to one terminal of the switch.

Wrap twenty-five turns of wire around a large nail.

Connect one end of the electromagnet to the free terminal of the cell and the end to the switch.

Close the switch. See how many small nails you can pick up. Find the average in three tries. Write it down.

How does it compare with the number picked up in *Activity No. 11?*

Why it works:

When we connect two dry cells in series, we get twice as much electricity than we do with one cell. That is, we get 3 instead of 1½ volts from one cell.

Then we can be sure that if we want a stronger magnet, we must send more electricity through the coils.

You will use:
  Dry cell
  Wire
  Switch
  Two nails
  Screw
  Piece of metal
  Block of wood

Do this:

Bend the piece of metal into the Z-shape shown in the diagram. Nail it on the block of wood.

Hammer two nails under the free end of the metal. Be sure the underside of the metal is not painted. Why?

Connect a long piece of wire to one terminal of a dry cell.

Wind the wire several times around the nail. Begin at the top of the nail and work downward.

Bring the wire across to the other nail. Wind it around as many times as before, working upward.

Connect the other end of this wire to one terminal of your switch.

Connect a second wire between the free terminal of the dry cell and the switch.

Close the switch. The sounder — the Z-shaped metal — will be attracted to the two nails underneath it.

You may have to adjust the sounder before it will work.

You have now made a simple telegraph sounder — and found a practical use for your electromagnet.

Why it works:

Electricity flowing through the coils of wire around the nails made the nails magnetic.

The sounder was attracted to the nails as long as electricity was flowing through the circuit.

The famous American inventor Samuel F. B. Morse, in 1844, made it possible to communicate with people in distant places by signals through the means of the telegraph.

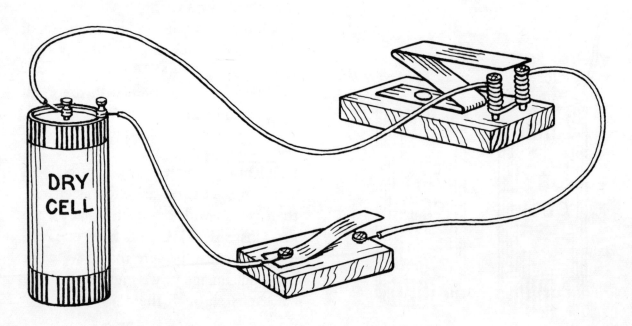

NO. 14. HOW CAN WE MAKE AN ELECTRIC CURRENT DETECTOR?

You will use:
- Dry cell
- Long wire
- Magnetic compass
- Block of wood
- Cover of small cardboard box
- Four thumbtacks
- Two paper clips

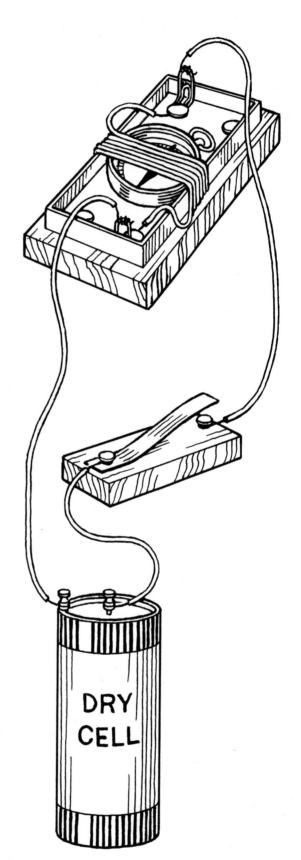

Do this:

Wrap about ten turns of insulated wire around the cover of a box.

Strip the insulation from the ends of the wire.

Place the box on a block of wood and secure it in place with some thumbtacks.

Bend two paper clips in half, as shown.

Wrap the ends of the wires around the thumbtacks. Slip the paper clips under the tacks before pressing them into the wood.

The paper clips will be your leads.

Place your magnetic compass inside the box.

Connect a wire between a dry cell terminal and a switch terminal.

Connect two other wires from the cell and switch to the paper clip leads.

Close the switch. The compass needle will move.

Open and close the switch several times.

Why it works:

Do you remember that when electricity moves through a coil, magnetism is all around it? That magnetism goes right through the glass to the magnetic needle and moves it.

Some of the important ideas presented in this book are summarized below. As you read them, you may want to go back and refresh your memory.

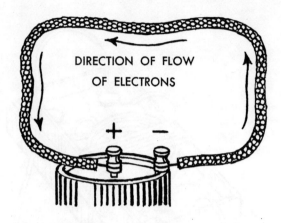

1. Electricity is made up of moving electrons.

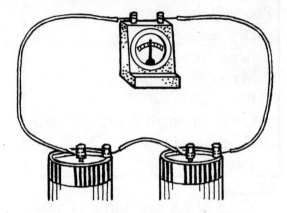

4. More than one cell connected in series will give more power than a single cell.

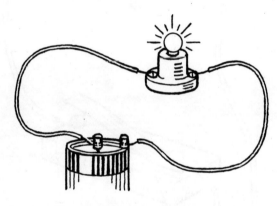

2. Electricity must have a complete circuit if it is to be used.

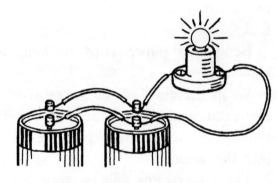

5. More than one cell connected in parallel will give longer life than a single cell.

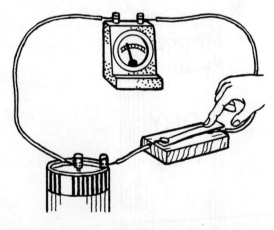

3. A switch is used to open and close circuits.

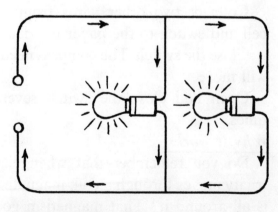

6. Lights in our homes are wired in parallel.

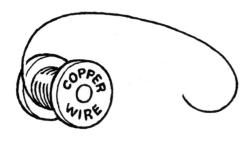

7. Some materials, particularly metals, carry electricity better than others. These materials are called good conductors.

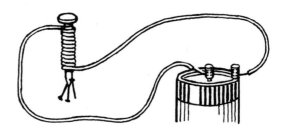

10. Electricity flowing through a coil of wire around an iron core, makes the core into a magnet for as long as electricity is flowing. This is an electromagnet.

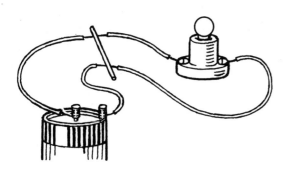

8. A short circuit occurs when the current can flow through an easy short cut instead of going through the regular circuit.

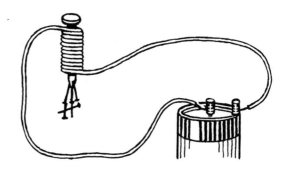

11. The strength of an electromagnet can be increased by increasing the number of coil turns.

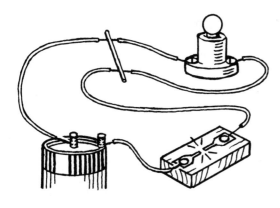

9. A fuse protects us from damage due to short circuits, or from using too much electricity at the same time.

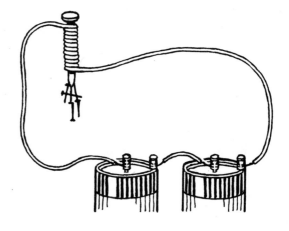

12. The strength of an electromagnet can also be increased by adding dry cells to the circuit.

SOME IMPORTANT TERMS
FOR YOU TO REMEMBER

Alternating current: An electric current that changes its direction very rapidly.

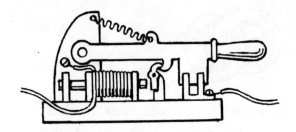

Ammeter: An instrument for measuring the strength of an electric current.

Ampere: A unit that measures the amount or rate of flow of electric current.

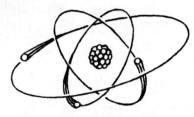

Atom: The tiniest part of an element.

Battery: Two or more electrical cells connected together.

Circuit: Entire path along which electricity can flow from the source through wires and appliances and back to the source.

Circuit breaker: An automatic switch which breaks the circuit when too much electricity is flowing. It is similar to a fuse, but it can be reused.

Compound: A substance formed by a combination of elements.

Conductor: A good carrier of electricity. It acts as a highway.

Direct current: An electric current that flows in only one direction through a circuit.

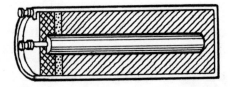

Dry cell: A combination of two different metals in a chemical solution that produces electricity.

Electrolyte: A solution through which electricity can flow.

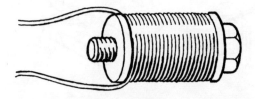

Electromagnet: A coil of wire wound around an iron core which becomes a magnet as long as electricity flows through the coil.

Electron: A tiny particle which carries a minus charge of electricity.

Element: A substance made up of only one kind of atom.

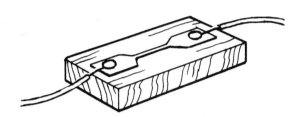

Fuse: A device which acts as a policeman to warn us of danger. The fuse melts when too many electrons are flowing. This breaks the circuit.

Galvanometer: An instrument for detecting direct currents of electricity.

Generator: A machine or dynamo that produces electricity from mechanical energy.

Horsepower: A unit for measuring power.

Insulator: A very poor conductor of electricity.

Kilowatt: One thousand watts.

Molecule: The tiniest part of a compound.

Ohm: A unit of resistance or friction that the electrical conductor has to overcome.

Ohmeter: An instrument that measures electrical resistance.

Power: The rate of doing work.

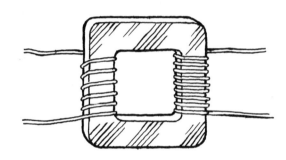

Transformer: A machine which can increase or decrease the voltage of an alternating current.

Volt: A unit that measures electrical pressure.

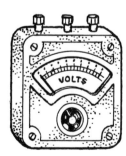

Voltmeter: A device for measuring voltage.

Watt: A unit for measuring electrical power.

SOME FAMOUS SCIENTISTS WHO MADE THE ELECTRICAL AGE POSSIBLE

Alessandro Volta (1745-1827), Italy, made the first cell that produced an electric current.

André Marie Ampère (1775-1836), France, developed the science of electromagnetism.

Georg Simon Ohm (1787-1854), Germany, worked with current electricity.

Michael Faraday (1791-1867), England, made the first electric generator.

James Watt (1736-1819), Scotland, invented the steam engine.

Samuel F. B. Morse (1791-1872), United States, invented the telegraph.

Alexander Graham Bell (1847-1922), United States, invented the telephone.

Guglielmo Marconi (1874-1937), Italy, first to send a message over radio waves.

Luigi Galvani (1737-1798), Italy, discovered that electricity is possible by chemical action.

Thomas Alva Edison (1847-1931), United States, invented the electric light bulb.

Hans Christian Oersted (1777-1851), Denmark, found that electricity and magnetism are related.

Charles Proteus Steinmetz (1865-1923), United States, made many contributions in the field of electrical engineering.

VOLTA

AMPERE

FARADAY

BELL

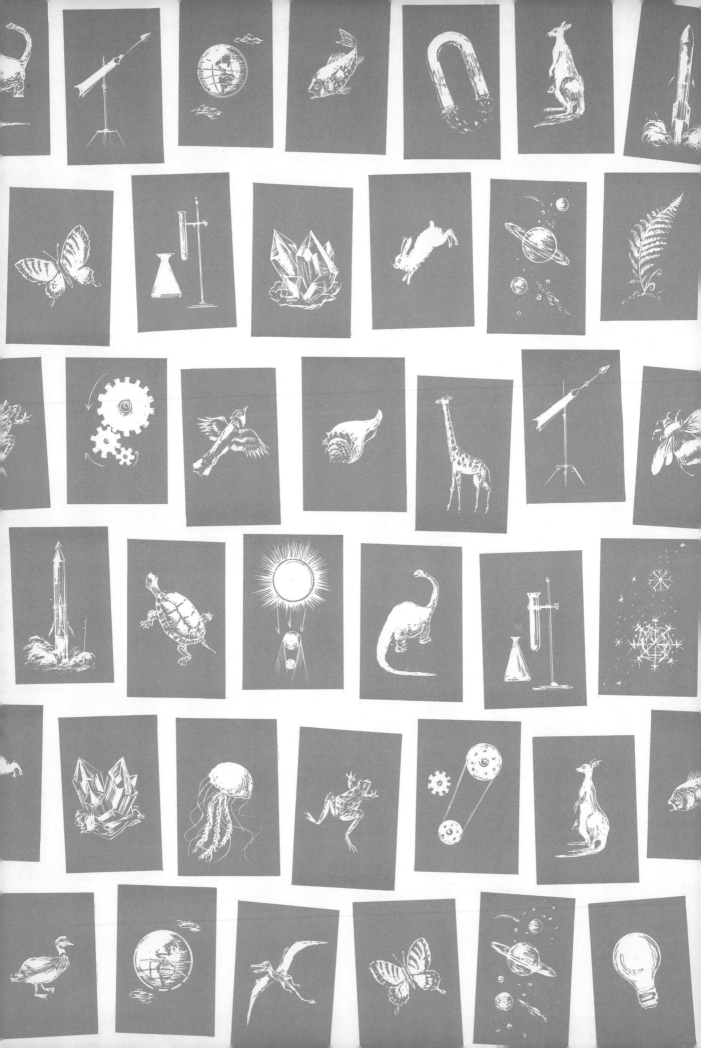

RONI SCHOTTER

That Extraordinary Pig of Paris

ILLUSTRATED BY DOMINIC CATALANO

PHILOMEL BOOKS
NEW YORK

To Monsieur Bill Kelly, a true lover of the pig, for Paris and friendship
and
To Monsieur Bill Hooks, for encouragement and inspiration
Merci—R.S.

To Patti Gauch, for all of her patience and wisdom—D.C.

MONSIEUR COCHON'S MENU OF FRENCH WORDS

Monsieur Cochon—Mr. Pig (say Meu-syeu Coe-shon)
Pig de Paris—Pig of Paris (say Pig duh Paree)
brasserie—restaurant (say bra-sree)
charcuterie—pork butcher shop (say shar-koo-teree)
joie de vivre—joy of living (say jwa duh veevre)
quai—an embankment along a river (say kay)
gâteau opéra—a rich, chocolate cake (say gat-toe ope-ay-ra)
tarte au pomme—an apple tart (say tart oh pum)
voilá!—there you are! (say vwah-la)
enfin—at last, finally (say on-fehn as if you had a cold in your nose)
jambon—ham (say jam-bon as if you had a cold in your nose)
comme ça—like that (say come-sah)
derrière—behind, bottom (say dare-ee-air)
attention—attention (say a-tahn-see-own)
Messieurs—gentlemen (say may-syeu)
Vive la loi!—Long live the law! (say Veeve la lwah!)
Vive la France!—Long live France! (say Veeve la Fronce!)
Vive le cochon!—Long live the pig! (say Veeve le coe-shon!)

With thanks to Madame Charlotte Silverberg

The artist used pastel, colored pencil, and watercolor to create the illustrations for this book.

Text copyright © 1994 by Roni Schotter. Illustrations copyright © 1994 by Dominic Catalano.
Published by Philomel Books, a division of The Putnam & Grosset Group, 200 Madison Avenue, New York, NY 10016.
All rights reserved. This book, or parts thereof, may not be reproduced in any form without permission in writing
from the publisher. Published simultaneously in Canada. Printed in Hong Kong by South China Printing Co. (1988), Ltd.
Book design by Gunta Alexander. The text is set in Bembo.

Library of Congress Cataloging-in-Publication Data
Schotter, Roni. That Extraordinary Pig of Paris!/Roni Schotter; illustrated by Dominic Catalano.
p.   cm.   Summary: A debonair Parisian pig finds himself in great danger when he falls into the clutches of an
unscrupulous butcher. [1. Pigs—Fiction. 2. Paris (France)—Fiction.] I. Catalano, Dominic, ill. II. Title.
PZ7.S3765Th 1994 [E]—dc20 92-26223 CIP AC ISBN 0-399-22023-2
10 9 8 7 6 5 4 3 2 1 First Impression

As everyone knows, the people of Paris love to eat, and Monsieur Cochon, though a pig, *was no exception.* He was a Pig *de Paris*, and, from the tips of his ears to the clefts in his feet, proud of it.

Early in the morning, Monsieur Cochon loved to stroll the broad boulevards and wander the narrow lanes of Paris, allowing his snout to lead him ever forward: to the bakery lined with long, brown arms of freshly baked bread…through the market piled high with cool, crisp vegetables…on to the crêpe maker to sniff the scent of his sugared pancakes, then a pause along the Seine to clear his nostrils, and, at last, when he could stand it no longer, to the *brasserie, for lunch!*

"Six mixed *salades* and a plate of truffles," Monsieur Cochon would command, his tail curling with pleasure. Or, if there was a slight chill in the air, two or three bowls of tangy onion soup.

Around him sat the people of Paris, talking, reading their journals, and dining on rabbit or chicken or some other poor animal's flesh. Monsieur Cochon always nodded politely to them and then shifted his gaze in another direction. For the truth was, the sight of his fellow animals cooked in sauce and set with a sprig of parsley on a plate was more than he could bear. Monsieur Cochon, you see, was a *vegetarian*, refusing to eat any and all meats.

Now, to be a vegetarian in Paris is an unusual thing; to be a pig in Paris is a dangerous thing. Monsieur Cochon crossed his legs. He was thinking of his feet. In Paris, in fact in all of France, they were considered a delicacy —breaded, or cooked in jelly!

Monsieur Cochon withdrew his pocket watch and glanced at it for reassurance. Engraved on the back were the words "Prudent Pig."

It was true; he was careful, ever on the alert for danger, avoiding all butcher shops, but most especially those shops called *charcuteries*, shops like the one across the street owned by evil Monsieur Découper and his assistant, Henri La Faim. For it was in places such as these that pigs could be found only on platters, turned into terrines, pâtés, and sausages.

"Putting on a bit of weight, are you, Monsieur Cochon?" Découper would call out from his doorway. "Very becoming," he'd snicker. Then he'd lick his fat, greasy lips, grin at Henri La Faim, and disappear into his terrible shop.

Just thinking of it made Monsieur Cochon shudder. He ordered a *café* and pastry to calm his nerves, then stared into his coffee and considered his fate. Would his life end on an oven rack? Should he run away? No use. Why, it was rumored that, even as far away as America, young boys and girls enjoyed sandwiches of boiled ham and cheese for lunch. No, Monsieur Cochon concluded, life lived without risk was not worth living. With the threat of a carving knife at your back, or a frying pan at your belly, you appreciated every moment and never took life for granted.

Rising from his chair, Monsieur Cochon pocketed the remains of his pastry and a few cubes of sugar, along with a thick crust of bread, and turned his dark thoughts to the sunlit afternoon.

Madame Sparrow and her family serenaded him from a chestnut tree. Monsieur Cochon broke off a piece of pastry and crumbled it onto the ground in tribute.

The pigeons leaning over to sip water from the gutter were his friends. Monsieur Cochon cast his bread upon their waters.

The horse carrying an officer of the law, though unknown to him, was a fellow mortal, so he stroked his mane and offered him a sugar cube.

Madame L'Âne, a donkey with whom he'd long been acquainted, brayed at him from her place on the square where she sold flowers from baskets strapped to her back. Monsieur Cochon saluted her, purchased a small sprig of lavender, and placed it in his lapel.

Full, happy, and overwhelmed with what the French call *joie de vivre*, Monsieur Cochon decided to walk off his meal with a lively-paced promenade. No dinner tonight, he thought, for even a pig must watch his waistline. He shivered as he recalled Monsieur Découper's greasy lips and Henri La Faim's threatening glances.

Crossing the river, he jogged briskly through the gardens of the Tuilleries, and trotted down to the *quai* by the pet stores, where animals imprisoned in cages waited to be sold.

All of a sudden, Monsieur Cochon was seized with an uncontrollable urge. While the pet shop owners turned their backs to argue the day's events, Monsieur Cochon carefully brushed the latch on a cat's cage, slipped the hooks on the chicken coops, and freed a family of ducks. Winking at an old bearded goat, he untied his rope, then unleashed a dog.

"At your service," Monsieur Cochon said under his breath to the grateful animals. And then, like a French Robin Hood, he disappeared silently down the *quai*.

In bed that night, hungry, Monsieur Cochon lay awake admiring the decorative molding on his ceiling. It reminded him of the cakes in the window of the pastry shop across the street from Monsieur Découper's store. Monsieur Cochon had only dared to view the cakes from afar, but even from a distance, he could see that they were works of art.

Monsieur Cochon rolled over and arranged himself in his sleep position. His thick black lashes closed, and he began to dream.

"Mocha," he sighed. Then, "Chocolate!" Monsieur Cochon startled awake. He had drooled on his pillow. Monsieur Cochon adjusted his head and fell back asleep, dreaming fitfully of macaroons.

Early the next morning, Monsieur Cochon awakened with one thought on his mind. "I have been good," he said, patting his waistline and admiring the way his britches fell loosely about his legs. "I would like a bit of cake. Perhaps…an entire cake. Yes, today, I *will* have cake."

Quickly arranging his beret on his head, Monsieur Cochon hurried out of his apartment. The vision of cake quickened his pace until he was rushing up one street, down another, then round the corner to a spot just across the way from the pastry shop run by Mademoiselle Le Sucre, one of the best bakers in all of Paris.

Here he came to an abrupt halt. Prudent Pig that he was, he dared not cross the street for fear of Monsieur Découper who, even now, was inside arranging his frightful wares for the long day ahead.

A billowing gray cloud swept across the Parisian sky. A breeze blew up and sent old newspapers sailing in Monsieur Cochon's direction and, with them, the smell of cake.

Monsieur Cochon stepped out into the street to better identify the odor. "Praline," he cried out in ecstasy. "With a hint of almond!"

Mademoiselle Le Sucre's cakes seemed larger now. Monsieur Cochon could see the details of each perfect sample—the graceful swirls of a mocha buttercream, the delicate shavings of chocolate crowning a *gâteau opéra*, the pleasing design the apple slices made circling a *tarte au pomme.*

Abandoning reason, forgetting the words "Prudent Pig," Monsieur Cochon was impelled toward the pastry shop window by a force greater than himself.

"Must have cake," he cried out. "*Need* cake!" he heard himself shout.

The pig in him was all-powerful now. Panting, snorting, and salivating, he pressed his snout against the glass of the pastry shop window.

Inside, Mademoiselle Le Sucre motioned to him, but she was not beckoning. On the contrary, she seemed to be waving him away! She was pointing, not to him, but to a place just over his shoulder.

Monsieur Cochon turned his head to discover what the matter was, when, suddenly, *all was darkness*!

Had he fainted? No, he thought, the darkness was too great. He was dead! But why then could he still smell cake?

Monsieur Cochon felt someone grab hold of his feet, the darkness crinkled around him, and he toppled thunderously to the ground.

"*Voila!*" a frightening and familiar voice exclaimed. It was Monsieur Découper, unmistakably, and the high stupid laugh belonged, without a doubt, to Henri La Faim!

What foolishness! Monsieur Cochon had no one but himself to blame. How weak and fleeting common sense was! How easily it could be laid low by a passion for cake.

Then, as suddenly as it had been taken away, light and Paris were restored to his sight. (Henri La Faim had removed what turned out to be a paper bag from his head.)

Monsieur Cochon lay on the ground, and before him stood his two mortal enemies. "*Enfin!*" Découper cried, licking his greasy lips. "Finally! The day of glory has arrived! At last you are ours, you succulent piece of pork, you juicy bit of *jambon!*"

Monsieur Cochon trembled. A moment ago he'd been dead, he thought, and sudden death with the ever-present smell of cake had not been so terrible. But death at the sweaty hands of Monsieur Découper and Henri La Faim was another matter.

Monsieur Cochon glanced down at his feet. They were bound together with a length of twine, and now Henri La Faim was attempting to tie up the rest of him. Monsieur Cochon squirmed and twisted, trying in vain to free himself.

"Calm yourself, you beautiful bit of bacon," Découper said. "No point in getting into a state. Henri will simply attach a hook to the twine at your feet and hoist you up with a pulley. *In short order*, you will be hanging by your feet, ready to be *cured* forever of your troubles."

At this dreadful joke, Henri La Faim dissolved into gales of stupid laughter.

Monsieur Cochon tried not to panic, but it was impossible. True to
Découper's word, in a minute or two, Monsieur Cochon was hanging
upside down, in plain view of all passersby. His beret tumbled to the ground.
Monsieur Cochon could not control himself: he squealed in humiliation.

"Henri," Découper called out. "Go into the alley. Get the carving knife."

Monsieur Cochon was frightened now, so much so that he didn't notice
a sudden darkening of the sky, failed to hear the strange fluttering sound
off in the distance, never realized that something *quite extraordinary* was taking
place in the city of Paris.

For witness to this scene of horror and defeat was Madame Sparrow,

who happened to be perched with her friends atop the lamppost in front of Mademoiselle Le Sucre's shop, hoping to catch a crumb or two from the people who passed in and out of the pastry shop. Madame Sparrow, the very same who, only yesterday, had serenaded Monsieur Cochon, to whom he had given a taste of his pastry.

At the sight of Monsieur Cochon's condition, she and her friends had flown off to *their* friends, the pigeons, the very same with whom Monsieur Cochon had shared his bread, and they to Madame L'Âne, and she had trotted off to the chickens he had freed, and they to the ducks, and on and on, until, before long, hordes of animals were converging on the scene.

In the alley, Henri La Faim had just reached for the carving knife, when a squadron of sparrows, led by Madame, circled around his head and landed in formation along his arm.

"Shooo!" he cried out, trying to wave them off, but the sparrows, used to balancing on the windy, wavy branches of trees, clung to his sleeve with little effort, chirping loudly.

"Henri!" Monsieur Découper bellowed. "What's that noise?" He glanced at Monsieur Cochon, who had lost some of his color. "Hurry with the knife. Our friend here is looking pale."

But Henri La Faim was too busy with other matters to obey Découper. From out of nowhere, a battalion of chickens surrounded him, clucking and scratching at his legs. Together with the sparrows, the sound they made was truly maddening. "Shut up!" Henri La Faim shouted at them.

"*Shut up?*" Monsieur Découper exclaimed in disbelief. "You speak to *me*, your boss, the owner of a respected establishment, *comme ça*, like *that*! You ungrateful fool. You…"

Découper never finished his sentence. For, just then, a pigeon landed on his head, another on his right shoulder, and one more on his left. Monsieur Découper stood stock still, like a statue in the park. "Henri!" he shrieked.

Out of the alleyway Henri La Faim finally came, running at top speed, pursued in the air by the birds, on land by the chickens, and now, at his heels, by a brigade of ducks.

"What's going on? What is this?" Découper cried out. He wriggled his shoulders and shook his head to free himself of the pigeons, but no sooner had he succeeded than they landed again, the one on his head pecking at his hair. "Go away," Découper screamed, but now he was surrounded by three hissing cats and half a dozen dogs, who nipped at his heels and jumped up, trying to bite his hands. "It's a conspiracy!" Monsieur Découper announced. "The pig is having his way with us. Get him!" Découper called to his assistant.

As strong as he was stupid, Henri La Faim managed to make his way toward Monsieur Cochon. With great difficulty he raised his arm, still covered with birds, and advanced toward Monsieur Cochon. "Prepare to die!" he called out.

Monsieur Cochon shuddered and bravely closed his eyes.

But before La Faim could do his dirty deed, from out of nowhere, the old bearded goat Monsieur Cochon had untied the day before appeared. Sneaking up behind Henri La Faim, he backed up, bent down, and butted.

The knife tumbled from La Faim's hand, and he flew through the air and landed at the door of Mademoiselle Le Sucre's shop, where, with her heaviest pie plate, she hit him full upon the head and knocked him unconscious.

It was exactly at this moment that Madame L'Âne, unnoticed in all the commotion, stepped behind Monsieur Découper and proudly delivered the greatest kick of her life, aimed precisely at the center of Découper's *derrière.* Up he sailed, somersaulting beautifully through the air, landing right next to his stupid assistant.

The crowd of spectators who had assembled to witness this amazing event cheered.

"*Attention!*" an official-sounding voice rang out.

"Make way!" another called.

The cats, dogs, chickens, ducks, pigeons, sparrows, and people all cleared away. Madame L'Âne and the old goat stepped aside. Two uniformed officers of the law arrived.

One of them read from a paper. "Monsieur Antoine Découper," he shouted. "Please step forward."

Découper staggered to his feet and saluted.

"Henri La Faim, rise!"

Découper leaned over and slapped his assistant awake, and he too managed to stand.

"This pig," the officer said, sounding angry, "about to be butchered out in the open air, on the very streets of our city. This pig...*Messieurs.* Have you a license?"

"License?" Henri La Faim repeated stupidly.

Monsieur Découper was unable to answer. He was suddenly seized with a terrible coughing spell.

"As I suspected," the official declared. "And so..." (His words were simple and, to Monsieur Cochon's ears, fortunately still part of his head, beautiful.) "...for attempting to kill an animal without a proper license to butcher, you are both, according to the law of France, 24th of July, 1881...under arrest."

The crowd went wild. Such cluck-ing, quacking, chirping, cheering, barking, and braying had never before been heard in the streets of Paris. Why, as far away as London, people stopped to wonder at the sound.

The officer picked up the carving knife, cut Monsieur Cochon's ropes, and…freed him.

"*Vive la loi*! Long live the law! *Vive la France*! Long live France!" the people shouted.

"*Vive le cochon*! Long live the pig!" Mademoiselle Le Sucre cried.

Monsieur Cochon blushed at this tribute, his wonderful rosy color now completely restored. He humbly bowed to the crowd.

"Are you all right, Monsieur Cochon?" Madame L'Âne asked him.

"Yes, yes. I'm fine," he assured her. "Only…perhaps a tiny bit hungry…."